THROUGH THE BILL PROMISED LAND WITHOUT EVER STOPPING

*

DEREK JARMAN

*Through the Billboard Promised
Land Without Ever Stopping*
by Derek Jarman

Published in 2022 by
House Sparrow Press, an imprint
of Prototype Publishing Ltd.,
Hackney, London,
England

www.housesparrowpress.com
www.prototypepublishing.co.uk

ISBN: 978-1-913513-32-0

A CIP catalogue record for this book is available
from the British Library

Designed by Theo Inglis

Edited by Jess Chandler and Gareth Evans

Printed in the UK by TJ Books

FOR KEITH COLLINS
(1966–2018)

CONTENTS

ON A ZEBRA SOFA, EATING
A MARRON GLACÉ

*

PHILIP HOARE

DEREK JARMAN'S WORLD IS LOST TO US NOW, lost in a glitter of tar pitch, emulsion and celluloid. It's a rich loss, stratified in glamour and poise, like the incandescent gardens of his childhood that seem to bloom in Technicolor like a Powell-Pressburger film. From the 1940s to the 1990s, his brief span, Jarman is forever caught in the biographical segue from austerity to resistance; from Home Counties schoolboy to secular saint. Like the artists he worshipped – Caravaggio, William Blake, Giorgio de Chirico, Paul Nash – Jarman's art was a physical echo of his sensual fantasy, a sunburst mirror of surreality versus gritty reality.

So no one would be surprised to see this surviving piece of fiction announced on a cinema marquee; a retrofit Arcadian Glamourama. It's a drive-in Saturday before the strange ones in the dome came along; a heartache in every dream home; a portal into Jarmanworld. In here, everything is beautiful, and you are welcome; the way Jarman embraced everything, as his friends will tell you. *Through the Billboard Promised Land Without Ever Stopping*: let's do it right here and now. The glory of Derek Jarman is that he always ran ahead of himself.

*

In the late 1960s and early 1970s Jarman painted a series of fantastical landscapes with strictly delineated horizons. They were much influenced by de Chirico's haunted cities and Nash's megaliths and pyramids; and by Jarman's own work on stage designs at the Slade, where the story of *Through the Billboard Promised Land* had begun as a play.

In one picture, entitled *Picnic*, discovered a few years ago in an attic in Bath, Jarman's pencil inscription reads, *Jan 26 Midday, elements for a picnic*. His birthday was on 31 January, perhaps the reason for this gathering on what looks like an industrial shore; the twin chimneys in the distance appear to belong to the power station at Tilbury, but the other amorphous shapes lend an alien dimension to the scene, like a drama waiting to happen.

Indeed, Jarman's notebooks for 1964 contain notes for a play provisionally entitled *The Picnic*, along with references to the Begum in flowered chintzes, who will appear in *Through the Billboard Promised Land*. That summer, Jarman left for North America, following his Canadian lover, Ron Wright, for his first experience of the States – one which would provoke this story. In the process, it became a kind of pastiche of his own preconceptions, a game; another level of fantasy.

Like these shapes and ghosts and lovers, like the endless horizons, Jarman's work of unscience fiction hovers between things; it can be anything you want it to be. Firbank on hashish; a Beardsley animation; Ken Russell and Pasolini on the beach; Samuel Taylor Coleridge's opiated despair in the desert; Ozymandias petro-collaged by Richard Hamilton. Kenneth Anger out of Jean Genet and Man Ray. Decadent? Divinely so. Sally Bowles's green fingernails curl round a Berlin door; Hockney's boys dive into the new pool; Duggie Fields's 1950s torsos twirl in an atomic whirl.

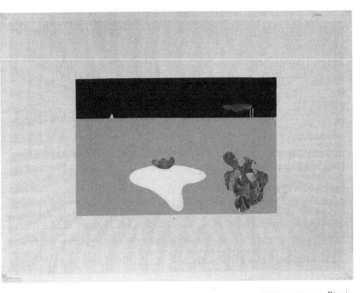

DEREK JARMAN, *Picnic*.

But it's also the Warholian mirrorcard cover of Jarman's book of poems, *A Finger in the Fishes Mouth*, published in 1972 by the Bettiscombe Press in Dorset. On the front is the complicit smiling face of a von Gloeden boy holding a flying fish. On the back are the words 'Thru The Billboard Promised Land', written in Jarman's elegant italic hand, as if preparing us for the forthcoming epic.

Jarman's mythical America, like his films, is a time-travelling, shape-shifting act of transformation, filled with arcane symbolism in the way that Blake wrote his own long poem, *America*, in 1793, turning the still new New World into an idealised prophecy, an apocalyptic place filled with angels and devils and creatures with silver thighs stalking New York and Boston and London and the Atlantis that lay between. Jarman's fantasy, too, is fired by that tense connexion. Jarman's friend and biographer Tony Peake observes that America's 'essential brashness was always at odds with his essential Englishness'. It is part of his power: the ambiguous eye of the artist, always caught in between states. His eclectic story invokes his Bankside warehouse apartment over the Thames with his greenhouse for a bedroom and walls hung with painted capes as if for superheroes yet to come. It's the silver witch ball hanging in the Crittal window of his 1930s Soho apartment like an advertisement for his alchemy.

His is the America of the post-war, Pop art imagination he had just discovered in person. When Marc Balet, a student from the Rhode Island School of Design, was given Jarman's number in search of work in 1970, he was told, 'He's the Andy Warhol of London.' 'That was good enough for me', said Balet, who was later to become editor of Warhol's *Interview* magazine. The meeting was another crucial step for Jarman: Balet would lend him his Super 8 camera, with which the artist would start to make his own films.

The whole of Jarman's life and work follows this same breathless dynamic. In an analogue, pre-digital world, his art was one long dialogue with himself and his collaborators, like Howard Sooley, who would receive phone calls at three in the morning from Derek, telling him about his new idea. In *Through the Billboard Promised Land*, we are just dropped into the middle of the story. Like its young King being led along, we don't know where we're going, or where it's all coming from.

Jarman is always moving on, wearing his Marks & Spencer jumper, his boilersuit or his sequinned gown (he was much shyer than you think), never waiting for the acclaim; he doesn't want to be pinned down. He is forever impatient, with himself. There is 'the sense', as Olivia Laing writes, 'that he was travelling in a private universe, sometimes alone and sometimes accompanied'.

*

So we wander with our protagonist, this unnamed, sightless young King whose eyes will turn to amethysts like Wilde's Happy Prince. Anything can be anything on this utopian shore, this Paradise Lost redesigned by Roy Lichtenstein. Camp and kitsch prevail. They are useful tools of insurrection and subversion.

Machines dispense peppermints for disabled people and the Begum's appearance has been 'much improved by delicate surgery'. Movietown is about to turn into the Land of Oz it always was. Jay Gatsby and Jack Kerouac might drive through with Bryan Ferry between Amanda Lear and Chelita Secunda in the back, under the giant spectacles peering at them through the dust. Meanwhile Crêpe Suzette sits on a zebra sofa eating a marron glacé in Biba's Rainbow Room high over Kensington High Street, while the flamingos in the rooftop garden all look the same. It's a literary acid trip, as Peake says, 'a virtual checklist of images and phrases central to [Jarman's] paintings and, later, his films'.

Languidly, everything seems set to repeat itself every day in this Promised Land, just in case you didn't catch it the first time. Everyone sighs when they hear the announcement, 'Tomorrow has been cancelled, ours are the golden pavilions of today.' The young King dances in diaphanous silks and satin tat like Andrew Logan rehearsing his inaugural Alternative Miss World on the Downham Road. You can all but hear the whirr of film running through Jarman's camera.

And the glorious seafarers wander the ocean, which is still clear and blue, and the young King continues his unseeing progress into the Billboard Promised Land. That's where this story will end up, on the fifth quarter, the last of England, in a cabin like Dorothy's, set down on a shingle beach as the King watches the pure blue screen, conjuring up images from this story that stay with him to the end. The chromium girls still dance and the world still plays at 45 revs per minute, going round and round and round.

Derek Jarman. 1971 —

my journey
Through the billboard promised
land   without ever stopping ~~it~~
~~You like   with John and himself~~
~~the king~~ +.

A fairy tale :
Grown Grown ups

THROUGH THE BILLBOARD PROMISED LAND WITHOUT EVER STOPPING

✳

DEREK JARMAN

ONCE UPON A TIME IN FARGO, caught between the one-armed bandits and the peppermint machines for the disabled, a high white villa was built to a perfectly comfortable design. A long white drive lined with tall cedar trees, perfectly still in the early morning sunlight, led up to a colonnade, newly painted, and above this a tympanum with sculpture, depicting the good deeds of the owner in pale pastel colours. The villa stood on the side of a long low hill, on the top of which a row of electric pylons had been gilded with pure gold leaf. At that high latitude the sun rose at midnight, and as the clock struck twelve, a slight breeze rustled the white net curtains and bent the tall green cedar trees. The sun peeped above the hill and sent long trembling shadows across the garden. The wind stopped; it was perfectly silent.

If you climb the eighty steps to the portico, you will find yourselves in white rooms of perfect proportion and geometry. The clock strikes twelve, a breeze blows the net curtains and a swallow flies in. He circles the room you have just entered three times and flies out again. The room is empty except for a large divan with curious and rare cabinets, supported by four silver dancing girls, automata of a perfection beyond description, who silently fan a young King in his sleep. The last chime dies away, and the young King stirs in his sleep, stretches his arms, yawns and is awake.

It is always like this, the young King thought. Here in Fargo nothing changes. The sun always rises at the twelve strokes of midnight, and a silent breeze flutters the curtains. He sat up in bed, and at once the four silver dancing girls started to sing a fresh morning song, as wonderful as the nightingale but more mysterious; and then, at the moment the song ended, the door opened and the King's valet came in, and they walked arm in arm down to the swimming pool to take their morning bath.

'John,' said the King, 'I am young and blind, and here in Fargo nothing changes, so today we will go on a journey with no destination, we will make no plans further than the end of the drive with the cedar trees, and you will lead me. We will leave this villa, which has been built to a perfectly comfortable design, where the lawns are green and nothing changes.'

And saying this he swam once more round the swimming pool, which was filled with Vichy water by the way, and walked slowly back to his room. The silver dancing girls had already started to issue orders for the journey, to prepare the golden car and the picnic hampers, but the King stopped them and said: 'Bandage my legs and arms, because I will go on this journey a poor beggar, and John will lead me.' And so dressed as a simple beggar, the beautiful blind King was led by John down the long drive, leaving the perfectly comfortable villa behind.

And as it turned out, no plans further than the end of the drive were possible, for the plain stretched so far that the horizon was in darkness, and down through the centre ran the Superhighway with its sodium lamps still burning in the pale blue dawn; and straight in front of them was a large sign which read 'Toutes Directions'. John looked round, but there was no other landmark in this plain, and nothing moved in the quietness. The only change was the increasing blue of the sky as the sun came up and the dark corners of the plain gradually receded. And then when the horizon itself seemed to disappear, the lights on the Superhighway went out.

But the young King saw none of this, for he was blind, and seizing John's hand he said: 'We will turn our backs to the sun and walk into the dark. That is the signpost we shall follow.'

And so for three days and nights they walked without stopping for food or rest; and on the fourth morning, straight ahead appeared a flock of pigeons arcing and wheeling around a vending machine, into which a large blonde woman was feeding coins. The Begum in flowered chintzes, for this was the lady's name, was of indeterminate age, much improved by delicate surgery – which had been perfected in this country to a state where even her fingerprints had been removed – and much addicted to charity; and here by the automatic vending machine, this passion found its most perfect expression, as with each peppermint thrown into the air she was greeted by a storm of applause which enveloped her like a mink coat. She didn't notice the two strangers arrive and continued to feed coins into the machine from a large purse; and when John interrupted her, to ask her where they were, she dropped it, and the coins rolled around her on the tarmac, and the pigeons, sensing the disaster, spiralled off into the distance.

'You are at the last outpost of Movietown, a great city,' she said. 'Do you need help?' she said, looking at the rags that the King was wearing. And then without waiting for them to reply she pulled out a pistol which was concealed between her breasts and fired a shot into the air. She winked at John. 'It's loaded. Can I give you a lift anywhere?'

John said that they had no particular destination and being very poor they had walked three days and nights. And so the Begum, whose charitable instincts were aroused, offered to show them the sights and give them lunch. They climbed into her car, and she turned the radio on so loud that further conversation was impossible, and they sped off down the Superhighway.

Movietown marked the frontier of the Billboard Promised Land, and as the Begum and her guests drove along the Superhighway, it gradually grew darker and the lights stretched out on all sides. Now everywhere were huge neon signs, which winked messages at the traveller; in fact they were so numerous that the street-lights were discontinued. The adverts were usually for lights in countless shades of colours, in crystal and chrome, in precious stones and metals, of different sizes, from lights the size of a matchhead to reflectors as big as a stadium. Sometimes huge signs flashed messages such as *In The Beginning Was God*, and an invitation to the *Villa Jesus Is Right*; while others announced the time, or details of fashion. In between the boards were great screens held by fine silver wires, which showed movies, for which, explained the Begum, shouting over the music, the city was famed, and from which it got its name.

She turned off the radio, but the music continued, for John saw that what he had taken for lamp standards were in fact loudspeakers, placed at regular intervals down the road. 'In Movietown,' the Begum continued, 'night had been turned into day, for the methods of communication we have perfected depend on light. And so it became increasingly difficult for people to function during the daylight hours, and now we are studying methods to prolong the darkness. We have already managed to cut the daylight hours down to five, and soon it might be possible to carry this further.'

They drove on a little further in silence, and then a sign appeared which was larger than any they had yet seen, and it said: *Astra Park: free parking, free love, free souvenirs*. And the Begum said they had arrived at the picnic spot.

Owing to the extension of night, flowers and trees had ceased to grow in Movietown, and the greatest ingenuity had been spent recreating this great park, the Begum said. And the Lawns of Paradise, where they were to picnic, were the latest extension. Here, scattered between the pink neon trees on silver lawns, were the living rooms of the past for rent. Plush sofas, cushions and antimacassars, vases of real tulips, chrome standard lights; the park had become the most fashionable meeting spot in Movietown, and rooms of any period or taste could be rented for an afternoon. The rarer the furniture, the more expensive they became, the Begum explained; that in the park it was possible to indulge one's selves in the most exquisite objects from the past, as the Lords of

Paradise possessed the greatest collection of any park in the world.

So they walked on the silver lawns between high silver litter boxes with neon arrows shooting into them, to an arbour of exquisite delicacy, where pale electric blue wisteria cascaded over the pink neon trees and a white peacock strutted. And in Wisteria Arbour, on the Lawns of Paradise, the Begum introduced them to Croquette and Crêpe Suzette, her two dear friends. Crêpe was sitting on a zebra sofa eating a marron glacé and reading a book which John saw later was called *Seconal and Diamonds*. She paid little attention to her arrival and gave them a cool 'Hi!', popped another marron glacé and curled deeper into her sofa. Croquette was more welcoming: seeing the beautiful King in his rags, she peeled off a white fur cape and sat him down on some cushions.

Meanwhile the park keeper arrived with the picnic hampers, and with small sighs of appreciation from her friends, the Begum unpacked the food and placed it on the table. The young King was silent and smiled gently into his darkness, and the perfection of his manners charmed the Begum, and after a while even Crêpe, who put down her book and sat a little closer to him. Then smoothing his brow with her hand, she said: 'What beautiful eyes you have,' and the King replied he was blind, and Crêpe blushed and said she hadn't realised, but the young King smiled and took her hand, and his manner charmed her.

And so on the Lawns of Paradise the picnic took place, and the Begum and her friends served the young

King and John his valet, and the moon came up behind the pink neon trees and the stars twinkled in the branches, and the park keeper walked through the picnic maze picking up paper from the silver lawn, smiling.

When the picnic was over the Begum drove them out of town to the Superhighway, and when they reached another sign which read 'Toutes Directions' she stopped, waved them goodbye, and switching on her radio so loud that any further thanks were impossible, turned, and drove back to Movietown.

At tea time they arrived at a great walled garden, and walking through the open gate they found themselves in strawberry beds planted in a vast geometric pattern between small clipped box hedges; and in the garden a sad Pierrot wandered carrying a long golden banner which weaved round him as he danced in circles and wailed: 'Owing to lack of interest, tomorrow has been cancelled, you are now in the strawberry beds of the eternal present.' And as he sang these words he danced and caught with one hand the sheets of a newspaper which turned slowly in the breeze, whirling the great events of the world over and over, over and over; and when he had caught them he smiled and threw them into the air again. Then he paused and spoke those same words again and again. 'Catch!' He threw John and the King a handful of the pages. 'Where are we, John?' asked the young King, as the pages floated round them; and John, unable to reply, stretched his hands up to welcome the sad Pierrot, but he gave a sign, and bowing, ran off down the path, and John and the King, hoping to explore further, followed him. And then, when they finally caught up with him, the whole event repeated itself, so that very soon they were both exhausted and sat down to rest in the warmth of the afternoon sunlight. Picking large handfuls of strawberries, they ate them, and after a while fell into a deep refreshing sleep.

'Are you there, John?' said the King. 'Can you hear the sea in the roar of the surf on the shingles embracing the earth? Can you see the white headlands and the white breakers in the sun?'

'Yes.'

'And can you hear the horses' hooves in the mimosa groves between the old sea walls worn by the wind, and the flowers, just look at the flowers of spring, the new nettles and dog violets. Listen to the sound of the blossoms dropping, the silent sounds in the dawn, the tangle of clouds which sorts itself out into new knots and collisions, sudden disappearances juggling in the sky. Are you here in the springtime by the sea with me, John? In the mimosa groves?'

'I am the Pierrot
of the present.
I am the Pierrot of the moment
Tomorrow has been cancelled
Ours are the golden pavilions of today.'

A dog barked off the shore, and there was a sound of preparation, and the Pierrot, down by the sea's edge, shouted up to the cliffs, and John and the young King came with him down to the shore.

Everywhere was laughter and the children danced round the ship as the sails were set and they plunged into the breakers. Oh! This is a tale of gardens, of flowers and of fabulous nights and dawns. The King's long hair blew in the breeze, gold and silver, and his clothes were transformed; the bandages fell away, and diaphanous silks and embroideries floated in the air and sparkled round him. And then a young girl came up to him with violets, which she placed on his eyes, and smiling he took them, and in an instant saw her and the ship with its pearls of light, and the colour of his eyes was dyed violet from this time on.

And the Pierrot sang of the young man with violets in his eyes, and John whistled and floated into the air, and the King followed him with his eyes, shouting: 'Follow, follow the seagulls, you are free, free.' And the air rushed about them, cold and electric, and the ship plunged on through the breakers towards the ocean. And John saw it was a garden, walled like the strawberry beds, with flowers of gold. This is a sacred valley, a garden of paradise, he thought. And the girl, who had joined them again, sat and sang of the golden flowers and insects, and they dived down to meet her through the spray; and she laid the King's head in her lap, and sang of the past and the glorious seafarers who had wandered the ocean, the perfect rings and the holy cup of life, and she called the King a Wanderer and sang his life. And John looked at the King and saw his eyes sparkle like amethysts.

And the girl sang: 'In the common silence of this world, the white poppies of my love are dancing,' and she called him Wellfound, Amethyst, and the violets whirled around him in a vortex, and John caught him in his arms and called him Amethyst.

And suddenly it was raining, and a rainbow stretched in a great arc in front of them, and the ship sailed through the centre of the arc, and the bands of colours passed over them reflecting in the rain, and they sailed into calm waters.

In the south, where the night sparkles with a score of stars for each of ours here in the cold north; phosphorescent sea creatures sparkle in the turbulence behind a ship, and glow secretly in the sand where a traveller places his foot. Now, in front of them, lay a pale coral sandbar, which wound like a snail's shell through the still jade of the sea, and the water at its rim sparkled with these silent sudden fireworks.

The young girl told the King that they had arrived at the path that would take them home; and they waded through the sea to the shore, and mysteriously the ship spun round and slowly drifted out of sight, and all the while they could hear the sound of the song praising the King's journey. When the ship had disappeared and the last notes of the song died away, they turned towards the shore and started to walk, slowly at first and then faster, until they were running; until they saw as they climbed the dunes two figures who beckoned, and found new footprints in the sand.

The sandbar stretched into a vast desert, and the small ripples where the wind had blown grew into mountains, and so they were caught in the vast tidal sweep of the earth. The sun set and rose, and in every step they seemed to grow smaller, and the sand expanded in all directions, now blotting out the two distant figures, now spreading infinite planes before them and cascading around them. And at last, when they seemed to walk in eternity itself, they stumbled up a dune to be greeted by the two figures who had always been before them; and recognising themselves in a moment which was like the clash of two great cymbals.

The sun had almost sunk behind the walls of the strawberry bed, and John looked at Amethyst the King, and he looked back, and they both laughed at the journey they had made in such a short time. And the Pierrot, who was sitting between them, winked and was silent. And when they said they must carry on their journey, he led them back through the strawberry beds to the gate on the Superhighway, and as they walked off to find a night's rest, they heard him start to wail: 'Owing to lack of interest, tomorrow has been cancelled.' And John and the King fell into a deep conversation about the strange events of the afternoon.

They had walked for several hours now, through this desolate landscape with its featureless wheat fields trailing off into the distance, and its flaccid undulating hills which were scarcely visible. It was a land to make a traveller despair, for on a journey one needs variety to please the eye and spur one's footsteps forward, but this monotony aggravated all those discomforts one finds on a long journey. Now they sat on the kerbside and felt a certain weariness in a world which seemed to negate their footsteps, where it seemed they were walking in a circle.

'The Pierrot should have accompanied us,' said the King, 'and he would have added a new dimension to his eternal present.' And he shrugged his shoulders and laughed. But the nature of journeys is not to sit on the kerbside and wait; even the traveller lost in the desert walks to find an oasis until his feet fold under him. And so, in spite of their weariness, after a few minutes they were on their way again.

Then at last their perseverance was rewarded; far away up ahead they saw a great conical hill which shimmered like a mirage, and as they grew closer it grew larger, unlike most hills, which deceive the eye and fall into a natural scale the nearer one approaches them. The hill grew larger, darker and more ominous, with a pall of cloud running off the top like a steam kettle, which quickly dissolved in the blue sky. And as they got nearer a great cacophony of sound assaulted them, twittering and thundering in that empty space like the roar of a thousand waterfalls with storms of starlings pelting overhead. John thought it must be some form of volcano, and in their excitement, they forgot their weariness and the hours of walking leapt by.

Now they were nearer, they heard a long, drawn-out sigh on which the great cacophony floated; a pall of dust hung over the land and the agitation was so great that the earth shook in response like the skin of a drum. For one hour they passed through an enormous car park before seeing any living thing, and then they saw a great army of people on their knees before the hill, staggering under the weight of countless objects which they were carrying on their backs. Men with drawn and resigned faces laboured under their heavy loads, and they wondered what sort of a place they had come to, where the people could make such sacrifice, walking on their knees without laughter or joy. They looked to see if there were any guards to enforce this obedience, but they could see no one and nobody broke rank. Nothing grew in this place, for the ground was pulverised by the knees of the supplicants, which had raised the pall of dust which they had seen from a distance. No one paid any attention to the newcomers, for in their dedication to their task they were oblivious to the two travellers who walked amongst them.

A break in the dust storm revealed the mountain, and John gasped, for it was entirely built with the offerings that the people carried on their backs, and in seven tiers it stretched towards the sky. They started to climb the great double spiral that circled the mountain in a landscape composed of objects of great age, the purpose of which had long since been forgotten. Now they were ascending through civilisation after civilisation, whose artefacts made the landscape of the great spiral, and through these centuries they accompanied the great tide of pilgrims, the latest to visit that place, carrying their offerings, cars and refrigerators and television sets, countless objects of plastic, and motorbikes. And up ahead a great jet plane which was being laboriously pulled up the steep ramp foot by foot. The ramp rolled upwards towards a cloud-capped peak of the mountain, and they joined the surging crowd in silence, and in the distance they could hear a whistling sound which slowly became intelligible to them, a loud muttering hiss which rolled round the mountain-top and echoed backwards and forwards: 'I am Topaz. I am Topaz.' It drifted around them and condensed in the cold high air. 'I am Topaz. Son of time passed. Meditator. Where are you travelling in the Billboard Promised Land? I am accelerating towards the stars. Where are you?' The voice swelled and echoed, sometimes it was behind you, sometimes up in front; then it detached itself above you and hung in that cold high cloud, and spiralled round until you felt yourself turning with it like telephone wires in a high east wind. And that mute sad crowd surged forward inch by inch into the mists. 'I am accelerating,' said the voice. 'I am growing. My feet are turning into miles, and the miles themselves into light-years. I am Topaz, ziggurat, monument and tomb.'

And now the road spiralled into the mist, and for a moment they stopped to watch the crowd pass by them, and catch their breath before plunging on. The King shut his eyes, and when he opened them, a white cat was sitting staring at him. Around the cat white butterflies danced, and the cat curled his tail into a question mark, and then an exclamation mark, and finally a comma; and by this sign indicated he would be their guide through the mists. And hand in hand they walked into the darkness, with a white cat and the butterflies showing the way.

I can't remember how far, or for how long, they walked, for in a way the journey never had a conclusion; and in the mists our friends were parted from those spectral travellers, and the friendly white cat led them through the crowds and into a dazzling starlight, and when they looked back the mists had parted and the great mountain they had climbed had disappeared, and the smell of sweet thyme which grew under their feet pervaded the place.

The sign over the door read:

The Tigers of Wrath are Greater than the Four Horses of Instruction.
Have you ever heard the one about the owl and the barracuda?
No?
Well, welcome to the Temple of Autodestruction.
Borgia Ginz, your host.
Pleased to make your acquaintance.
Beware of pickpockets.
Coats are left at the owners' own risk.
And now, ladies and gentlemen, the act you have all been waiting for.
The moment of greatest suspense.
When Mr Borgia Ginz takes up the pieces and presents you with that rarest event: a complete person.
No sticking tape.
No glue.
This is no mean trick.
And Sir Pa Sir Cur.

His accompanist, descended on his father's side from the Apostle John, and on his mother's from Mary, who was also the Mother of God, whose epicene descendants, the weak side of the family, provide the staff and took your coat at the door, will show you that the box is true and sound, and has four sides.

And now, if you will step into this paper bag.

Sir Pa Sir Cur will wave the wand whilst the Mage broods over the bright past.

Bang and Hey Presto!

Abracadabra!

By the Most Solemn Seal of Solomon you are here atomised in the dust that sparkles in the sunlight, or should I say the beam of the phantom projectionist: Borgia Ginz.

Poisoner of all flowers.

The white cat sighed, put her tail between her legs and slunk round the door, the butterflies followed one by one, they were alone at last.

The building is amazing, the building is a maze, the Temple of Autodestruct.

'Oh! There you are,' said the Begum. 'You know my friends Bellevue and Honeymoon. Belle is engaged to Sir Pa Sir Cur you know? Belle is dressed in a bikini by The House of Sobriety made entirely of black flies. The first course is soused cobra, black coffee into acid served on crushed velvet disposables.'

A sow walked across the table and Belle jumped on her back, and rode up and down, trampling the iced buns;

the sow finally sat down on the great pyramid, whilst the daughters of the Mother of God rushed around with mops and dusters to save the second course. 'Well done Belle!' whispered the Begum, paddling her tits in the soup. Borgia Ginz killed the sow with a look and the daughters served her to the guests. 'Oh Lord!' said the Begum. 'I've lost them.' And balancing on the rim she finally decided to take the plunge.

'Now for the intermission,' said Sir Pa Sir Cur. 'An old one you will all remember.' And immediately the roof rolled back with an ominous sound, and rose petals started to fall on the guests.

'This is an extremely difficult trick to perform, may I remind you,' said Borgia.

'What a way to go!' said the Begum as she surfaced for the second time.

'Wait, I'll get you my snorkel,' said Honey.

'Aha!' said Sir Pa Sir Cur, as he tapped the box. 'The romance of the Romans.'

The petals increased to a blizzard.

'Whee!' said Honeymoon, twirling them into the air.

'Is this an orgy?' said Belle, dusting herself with DDT.

'Blow your mind and blow your neighbour', was the motto on the cracker. The rose petal drifts whirled around them. Sir Pa Sir Cur announced the cabaret, tricks so sublime that in the past they had only been performed by gods and the like.

Borgia Ginz, famous drag act, Lotus of Hong Kong, Charm of the Orient, and lastly, and most memorable,

Scylla and Charybdis, for which the daughters will take on the form of savage dogs.

A group of black and white monks appeared, with spotted dog faces, men of India who growled and licked the feet of the guests; a small orchestra, concealed in the Winter Garden, started to play a wistful melody; and the dogs danced exotically, revealing slowly their dark lithe bodies.

Honey started to dance with them, and Belle followed her; then the Begum climbed out of the soup shouting: 'Service! Service! Oh to be balled by a Dalmatian. Have you heard the one about the socialite and the Mars bar?'

'We are living in the zoo of an instant palace,' said the King to John.

'With this baton rouge I will tap the box with four sides and reveal to you Jean Machine and Mr Dream, hero and heroine of a thousand fucks, slot machine, cartitex and gamble your oats, Jean of the zippers and seamless stockings, a Mr Dream cocksman, lock up your sons, he's screwed from here to the international dateline and never missed a trick. And now if you'll all hold hands we'll sing the anthem and welcome our friends Jean Machine and Mr Dream.'

The box exploded like a silvered floodlight, and the amazing fashionable couple stepped out amongst the guests, glittering and irresistible.

'Animal, vegetable or mineral. I'm a diamond potato beetle from Colorado, shall I come to the fancy dress ball straight or frying tonight?' he said.

Teetering along the green, long catwalk, he plunged into the lily pond.

'Jean, have you anything to say to the guests?'

'Is your world playing at 45 revs per minute?' She blew a kiss, and her pink gellee lips detached themselves and smudged the cheeks of her adoring audience.

'I love you all!' she cooed, and swallowed a gold fish finger with an exquisitely delicate gesture.

Mr Dream floated amongst the lily pads like an iridescent oil spot, and his body curved and twisted with the ripples; and Jean Machine wound herself up so tight that the orchids on her black net dress wilted, and one by one the petals collapsed onto the catwalk, and in a minute she wore only her famous seamless stockings.

'Home is where the hard is!' she shouted, and dived through the shimmering rainbow on the lily pond, and disappeared in a climax of tiny diamond bubbles which floated briefly on the water and slowly, one by one, sank out of sight until not a ripple was left, and one by one the guests followed her until no one remained.

And after Borgia Ginz had taken his bow, the daughters of the Mother of God rushed around opening the doors and windows, and the vast building was filled by the whispering sound of sand in the desert; and John and the King watched as the dawn sun sparkled through the great windows in great dust shafts, and slowly, as they watched, the great building crumbled back into the desert, until when they finally left, the place where the great temple had stood was only marked by a sand dune.

THE YELLOW EMPRESS WAS SO BLIND she was unsure of herself, and so cruel that her subjects went in fear of her, and so vain she was the ugliest person in the world, but she was fond of dancing. Conversation at her court was in superlatives, and the whole court preoccupied themselves in the discovery of new ones. Honours were conferred for adroitness in this pursuit and the highest office in the palace was the editorship of the *Imperial Superlative Dictionary*. The court spent their days dancing, the evenings and nights in gossip and distractions. The favourite dance at Court was the St. Vitus, as the Empress excelled in this and no one could be seen to equal her. After breakfast, which was a longish sort of meal, the dance would begin, and the search for superlatives would be undertaken. All in all, it was a tolerable sort of life.

The Yellow Empress was a star in the Billboard Promised Land and one of the chief hostesses of Movietown. Her slightest movement was recorded for posterity, and she would smile and say the next generation would spend so much time watching her that they would forget to lead their own lives, and so, with my deathbed film, the world will finally end. This tale would always please the Empress, and after telling it to the court at breakfast each day, she would burst out into peals of hysterical laughter, which never failed to reduce the company to complete silence. At which point, the great golden doors of the dance hall would open and the old lady, surrounded by her maids of honour, slowly descended the staircase with a little pause here and there for photographs, and the orchestra struck up the refrain of the St. Vitus Overture.

This morning the Empress appeared at breakfast late, for in her blindness she had mistaken a cup for a hat and fixed it to her hair by a toothbrush; the operation would take a long time, and the maids of honour had left the old lady alone in fear of her anger. The three scarlet rouge dots on her pale white face seemed more than usually bright as she sat down, wrapped in yards of yellow gossamer spangled with silver sequins, and handed her two ivory walking canes to her eye and confidant, Miss Century Fox.

Miss Century Fox was even older than her mistress, but was all-seeing, and reported daily the court intrigues, the lapses of etiquette and love affairs with which the court amused itself. She ruled the court and her smile invited pleasure, whilst the slightest frown spelt disaster. For the old Empress, although vain and cruel, was above these daily affairs of state. Miss Century Fox was also the chief historian of the Empress's court. Although not a lexicographer, she edited the historical journal *Hemline*, in which the affairs of state were reported, and was also keeper of the film archives. This morning she had invited her friend the Begum to bring the young King Amethyst to the dance.

As the King and John, his valet, sat on the sand dune, they were surprised to see a helicopter approaching, and the sound of music which gradually grew to a crescendo, over and above which the Begum's voice could be heard. 'Climb on up,' she cried, and a ladder swung down from the machine. 'Hi,' said the Begum. 'Have you met my friends, Crêpe and Croquette?'

'Crêpe is extremely fashionable and Miss Croquette isn't,' she said with a smile. 'How do you like the sounds? It's the *Music of the Spheres*; all helicopters are now equipped with these recordings to make flying the pleasure it really is. I'm going to take you back to Movietown to meet the Yellow Empress, who has heard of your journey and wishes to meet you.'

And without further word she pulled throttle and the helicopter sped along on its cushion of decasonic sound, over the sands, until John and the King saw the Superhighway and then in the distance the great shimmering hulk of Movietown, rising up step by step into the sky with the pall of night hanging over it, and the myriad twinkling lights for which the city was so famous.

They arrived just as the Yellow Empress was descending the staircase, and when she reached the bottom she placed both her ivory canes in one hand and with great deliberation held up the other to be kissed, and then without pausing for a moment carried on into the ballroom, as if the whole incident had been but a small comma in the long paragraph of her day; and Miss Century Fox shook them both by the hand and looked at them in such a way that one could hear the pages of *Hemline* turn in her mind.

They danced through the day: the tango, the rhumba, then a Charleston or two, a twist, a shuffle and the St. Vitus. Every now and then a whistle was blown and the whole company stopped for light refreshments. A golden table was wheeled in, piled with candies and gateaux, plates of pink sugar pigs in groves of marzipan pine trees, elaborate castles with ladies in high pointed hats and spun sugar veils waved to iced knights on lollipop chargers, large jelly mountains quivered sympathetically to the music.

The Empress squinted into her shadows and sighed, and without another word the dance would begin again, and her tiny feet in egg-glass slippers spun her through the crowd, for the Empress always danced alone in her precious dancing shoes. Rumour had it that many years before she had lost one of them at a débutantes' ball given by one of the oldest families in Movietown, and had gratefully danced with a young prince who found it, but no one could quite remember the details of the story, and the edition of *Hemline* which would have related the story had been mislaid. Now the glass slippers were closely guarded, and each day a member of court was given the task of watching over them.

John and the King watched enchanted as the guests arrived, two by two. They hardly dared breathe a word, lest this world of dream that the Begum had brought them to should slip away. For now in front of them were all the kings and queens of history: Caesar and Cleopatra, Nero and Messalina, Genghis Khan, Charlemagne – one by one they entered dancing; Catherine of Russia with a group of guardsmen, Elizabeth of England, Philip of Spain, Richard the Lionheart, St Louis of France. And now the orchestra played a new tune that was a great compilation of past songs that this pantheon had laughed and made love to.

And so they danced, on and on, in an infinity of graceful turns, a spiral of glittering confetti, which slowly unwound through the cavernous spaces of the great ballroom, bubbles in the champagne of history, twinkling for their moment. And the old Empress laughed and laughed and kissed them all, and Miss Century Fox silently entered them into her journal *Hemline*, and the old Empress laughed and laughed and kissed them all until the chandeliers twinkled and tinkled and John and the King Amethyst stole out into the night.

If you take the path to the left of you and leave the Superhighway several miles further on from the oasis, which is called Aqua Vitae, you will come to one of the greatest treasures of the Billboard Promised Land: the ruins of the city of Disc. The sacred city of Disc now lies in the desert, but was once the hub of a great civilisation, which is a constant source of speculation to archaeologists. So mysterious are its remains that from time immemorial it has been the object of reverence and fascination, the source of plunder and a fount of controversy. The abundance of its archaeological remains are only equalled by their fragility; and indeed much of the fascination of this civilisation lies in this evanescent quality. Objects of great rarity, rescued from the sands, crumble in sunlight, and the archaeologist has only seconds in which to appreciate his finds.

The city itself is the haunt of poets, and its vibrations have insinuated themselves into dreamers' minds throughout the centuries. The literature of the Billboard

Promised Land is based entirely on that of the city of Disc, and fragments from that golden age are treasured, emulated, but never equalled. The city was once openly plundered by tourists and the few desert people who gained a precarious living in its remains, but now was protected with a vigour unequalled in any other land. Absolute silence is demanded of all visitors so that their presence does not upset the poets who are directing the excavations, silently sitting with expectant tape recorders and microphones whilst the students of literature quietly brush the earth with sable brushes to release the precious fragments of the past. Digging can only proceed on the calmest of days, and rain and wind, which destroy the finds even quicker, bring all work on the site to an instant halt.

After a simple breakfast of bread and figs, which the golden-eyed boy provided, John and the King started to walk down the Superhighway, and when they arrived at the turning to Disc, they took it. John had purchased a *Guide Bleu* in Movietown and as they walked along the road he read it aloud to acquaint themselves with the city and its history. The archaeology of sound has only been perfected in the last decades and the systematic exploration and cataloguing of archaeological remains was, until recently, undertaken in a haphazard way; material of great value has therefore been lost to the world, but now this situation has been rectified and a twenty-four-hour monitoring service is in operation to record the slightest sound.

Disc is situated ten miles from the oasis of Aqua Vitae, down a narrow and ancient road. The site is spectacularly placed on a white limestone outcrop which forms a U-opening into the desert. On your left about two miles down the road you will come to the remains of the aqueduct and canal system which fed the city with water from the Well of Memories in a deep cleft in the rock. The well itself is surrounded with fig trees of great age and if the traveller is lucky he will see the white desert phoenix which floats motionless on the eddies of air high on the cliff face. The remains of the aqueduct itself will give the traveller a foretaste of the exquisite remains of the city. Several arches still stand to a height of fifty feet built in the finest rock crystal from the mines at Lapis, fifty miles distant in the desert.

John and the King passed the shimmering remains of the aqueduct. Leaving the aqueduct behind, the road starts to descend, the guide said, and one mile further on you reach the lodge, where a small restaurant provides refreshment before the traveller carries on into the ruins. It is advisable to stop and rest, as any adequate visit will take at least a day. Taking the advice they stopped briefly, and hiring felt overshoes, they walked on to the gate of the city.

The entrance to the city was protected by a labyrinth of great complexity, the key to which was known only to the city and its guardians. The labyrinth was built of crystal and mirrors which caused the most terrible distortions in the sunlight and disorientation at night. Anyone unlucky enough to lose their way will be doomed unless they are rescued; great snakes will be dropped into the invader's path, and these magnified by the mirrors and the claustrophobic surroundings had created the legend of dragons of monstrous appearance which guarded the city and drove an intruder to madness. The maze refracted and reflected the sunlight into myriad small rainbows until the senses became so disoriented it was quite possible to realise why the city of Disc, in all its long history, had never been attacked with any success. Now, mesembryanthemums glowed in hot crevices in the crystal walls, as John and the King followed the arrows which indicated the path.

In the centre of the labyrinth was a deep blue lake. Here an old poet, with a face tanned by the sparkling sunlight, kept watch over the goldfish who swam in flotillas through the water. In the past, visitors had been required to swim the lake before they were able to continue into the city, leaving their old clothes behind; then they were greeted by priestesses who guarded the entrance.

It was an old legend that before the division of light and darkness, Helios with his six companions had invaded Disc, attracted by its great luxury; but lost in the mirror maze, the young sun god was maddened by his own burning and distorted reflections, until finally he had stumbled blinded out of the maze, and had dived into the blue lake. And in this way night was created and the fish who swam in the lake were dyed gold; and the young god's rays had imprinted themselves on earth, and from that time forth man had discovered gold.

And now the old poet sat by the lake watching the ripples in the water where the goldfish swam, and listening, for every now and then a word or a phrase would escape where the young god had cast his golden shadows in scintillating sparks. A poetry of fire, which cast the whole place momentarily into darkness with the brightness of its reflections. He bent over his recording equipment and listened.

> He combs
> The golden rays
> Cooled by breezes from the four corners
> The swallow has risen (in the east)
> The doors are open
> Mankind is awake.

The words flew into the air and John and Amethyst ducked as they exploded in showers of sparks, but the old poet hardly noticed, so that the burning fragments singed his beard.

The poets of the sulphur baths in seven crystal tiers, star shaped, with the laughter of ghosts in its waters, waited expectantly. The water also released its treasures, and one of the young students motioned John and Amethyst aside and played him the day's finds.

> Here watch a butterfly trapped in a glass
> The sand pours in
> Until white wings flutter into stillness
>
> Six times three minutes
> Archaeologies

Burning in high winds
One last walk
One last look.

Further on there were other poets studying a whirlwind of shadows which issued from a deep well;

'a picture wind on the sea',

'washing one's hands in the sun',

'into my line of vision',

were some of the slogans they heard.

All of these occurred whilst John and Amethyst walked in the city of Disc kicking sand ahead, perhaps just a gesture under the blue skies. It was a great joy to walk through the great sulphur pools with their laughing sighing waters, and the poets mingling with the shouts of the bathers' ghosts, debating the outcome of the battle between love and chastity which was fought at the vernal equinox each year many years ago.

They were on their way again and leaving Disc in the evening they arrived at a cool oasis and sat down to rest. The desert shimmered pink in the evening light and the palms touched by sweet breezes cast inviting shadows, hung with scarlet bougainvillea which trailed in the water. John dipped his fingers in and touched Amethyst the King's forehead. Suddenly the quiet was interrupted; two boys were struggling in the water, the peaceful world of reflections swayed and broke into pieces as they fought. Lines of scarlet and green snaked across the water, and the peacocks in the palm trees shrieked.

Then, as quickly as it had happened, all was quiet again, as they ran off into the dark mysterious undergrowth, like golden dragonflies silently darting among the reeds.

Now Amethyst the King was sleeping, and John, his valet, kissed him, and shutting his eyes threw back his head in the sunlight. Tall funereal cypress trees shrouded innumerable broken statues, obelisks and urns, piled one on top of another, every now and then an avenue opened out but led nowhere, for this dead world resembled a spider's web into whose vortex the unlucky monuments of past glory had been snared. On all sides, cascades of broken statuary piled up, so the very daylight seemed shut out. Their footsteps echoed in the silence, which was occasionally broken by the steady sound of dripping water and the clatter of stone chips dislodged by their feet. Huge, unseeing eyes stared up at them. Locks of stone hair permed forever, massive hands with broken fingers pointing vacantly to the sky. No lizards scuttled into these crevices or flies warmed themselves on the stones, as the blue of the sky was as cold as ice and cast a deadly chill. Hoarfrost glittered in gaping mouths and tightened its grip on marbled torsos. Here was the broken statue of a great emperor on horseback, there a great winged bull. A pathway opened ahead of them, meandering between precipitous cliffs of marble fragments, which glowed an unearthly blue in that cold light. Deeper and deeper they travelled into the twilight. Now they were in an avenue lined with tall obelisks which resembled the deepest recesses of a pine forest.

A great space unfolded itself, a huge stadium, surrounded by cascades of marble statues on all sides. John and the King walked into it. Two knights in mirror armour, with enigmatic masks, were playing a game of tennis and ignored the intruders. The moon hung high above them and a light drift of snow fell over that place and muffled even the sound of the ball. The white cat stalked across the stadium followed by the butterflies, who shimmered in the moonlight; her green eyes blazed for a brief moment and the moon set in them.

The pyramids rose out of the snowy plane. Men in dinner jackets with white ghostly faces are crawling towards them. The bride is sitting in front of a wedding cake of ice; she looks at herself in a hand mirror, she closes her eyes. Borgia hands her a card and kisses her neck. Drops of blood form where he kissed her; they immediately freeze, they are rubies. A man with a black rhinoceros horn on his head places them round her neck.

John and the King watched the frozen waves for two or three minutes in silence. A naked boy with dark hair and golden eyes is flying a black kite which eclipses the sun; four pebbles splash into the water, there is the sound of a jet passing overhead. The boy lies drowned at the water's edge, his hair floats in the water, the black kite skims and flutters listlessly above the water. A group of children in paper masks are doing acrobatics; a wave detaches itself and moves a fraction before freezing again. A tear falls from the boy's eye and clatters in the shingles.

The pyramids are great reflectors and the sky is mirrored in them. They contain all time mirrored in them; they are burning blue cold flames which freeze in the night with the sound of breaking glass. The sphinx has written in her eyes, 'Silence is Golden'; John and the King run towards her; there in a large and empty room, the bride cuts the wedding cake of ice and it catches fire. The guests laugh, the sphinx smiles.

The boy with black hair and golden eyes is dressed in the rubies the bride has given him. He walks backwards towards Movietown. He is an emperor and John and Amethyst the King join the crowds who follow him. He smiles with the art of mirrors. They drift into a whirlwind with him. He dances in the flying ice particles with his hands on a tambourine. The moon glistens in the ice particles; it is cold, waves break into green waves in silence and all around the blue fire, with the smashing and splintering of glass. The pyramids are reduced to a pile of sapphires, and now it is the turn of all history; the marble statues scream until they shiver into fragments and the endless desolate landscape is covered with snow. The boy with black hair and golden eyes laughs and rides through the swirling snowdrifts on a black charger.

A stone plopped into the water and John opened his eyes. There was laughter in the shadows around the oasis, how fireflies drifted in the bougainvillea. A great yellow moon threw the King into high relief, like a pharaoh contemplating tributes from countries beyond the edge of the world. The King shivered and the golden-eyed boy wrapped a cloak around him. After the old order, a figure staggers through the blinding drifts to be faced with the gate through which he must pass. The Pharaoh eyes him through the grass by the frozen sea; the grass sparkles in the wind, a circle is drawn by a fountain, the fountain spurts jets of stars, a dark sun crushes the world into ashes which blow in their face. A red moth flutters and dies by the Pharaoh's hand, which is burning on the icy sea. The Pharaoh sighs and looks into the mirror. He kisses the bride; flowers bloom in the snow, they freeze and crumble into dust.

The men in dinner jackets are scrabbling among the sapphires into which the pyramids have crumbled. They are filling their pockets with them, but the blue fire encircles them, and they burn.

The Pharaoh is by the seashore; he stoops by the drowned boy to pick up a tear. At four in the morning the fireflies extinguish their lights, and a deeper silence envelops the oasis before the first mutterings of the dawn chorus. The moon turns white and shrinks before the dawn. This is the shadow of the night. John and Amethyst sleep.

The ice has enveloped the world. Golden-eyed boy wheels on a black charger, he sparkles with icy diamonds. The frozen waves have blown in the eye of the storm; lightning spirals round them like a Catherine wheel. The flotsam and jetsam of civilisation glimmers briefly in spectral fires deeply embedded in the ice. The whole scene fades into darkness, the waves have formed a labyrinth in the sun's shadow. The last bird has sung. Colour has deserted the world.

The old lady sat amongst her mementoes with the blinds drawn in the hot afternoon. Nothing moved in the room except the bubbles in her mineral water, and then she started to laugh; in the distance the orchestra still played the heavenly tunes of the past, and she waited, surrounded by her mementoes, for her friend, Miss Century Fox, to announce that John and Amethyst the King had returned.

The drive to the Perfectly Comfortable Villa is overgrown with brambles. In the hot September afternoon the flies buzz on the fermenting blackberries and crawl, drunkenly, along the cracks in the stucco. A car from another age stops in front of the iron gates. An ancient hand lifts a black veil, memories flood into the silence. It's only a moment and the car passes on, and now who remembers the Perfectly Comfortable Villa?

It is said that in the dawn light of that day, an angel with golden eyes set out over the desert beyond the mines of Lapis and disappeared into the west with Amethyst and John, his valet.

Or there were other ends. Maybe they dreamed of Disc too long by the oasis that night and disappeared into the past with the angel as a guide. Or maybe Movietown itself disappeared into the air like the other treasures of Disc, and John and Amethyst the King with it. I've heard of several other rumours, but I like the first one most, and believe that when we are old, we will be invited to tea at the Perfectly Comfortable Villa; with the Begum and the Yellow Empress and Miss Century Fox we'll be able to enter their stories of the travels in the west into her journal *Hemline*, and we will all listen, entranced.

Through the billboard promised land.

Once upon a time in Fargo, caught between the one armed bandits, and the peppermint machines for the disabled: a high white villa was built to a perfectly comfortable design. A long white drive lined with tall cedar trees, perfectly still in the early morning sunlight, ~~painted green~~ led up to a colonade newly ~~painted~~ and above this a tympanum with sculptures depicting the good deeds of the owner. ~~painted in pale pastel colours~~

. The villa stood on the side of a long low hill, on the top of which a row of elefric pylons had been gilded with pure gold leaf.

At that high lattitude the sun rose at midnight; and as the clock struck twelve a slight breeze rushed the white net curtains, and bent the tall green cedar trees.

The sun peeped above the hill and sent long trembling shadows across

The battle between love and
chastity
flames and tears.
a reptile in the glass
a sea of pure silver
scintulating sparks
a picture of wind in the scan

ALMOST
ORDINARY
ERUPTION.

the green leaf devours
the sun

a description of the labyrinth
of crystal which is necessary to pass
thro distorting mirror. the blue
pool with goldfish and the nuns of
the bank van. The theatre
and the fight between love and chastity
the 4 winds.
A twister at or spins

the centre

In the common silence of the
                                world
The white poppies of my love
                          are dancing

✓

_____

Now I am sailing on this
                    rocking chair
back back to where tomorrow
Washes the pavilions of today.

✓

michael jarman 64 priory rd nw6

Topaz Ludwig: songs · organ musick

The picnic · monologue · descent

monologue   Topaz the wandering

few through out   bill board promises

land   to learn ...

flowers   contrast

             scene 1 curtain on dark

stage then neon lights start flashing on

and flickering until the whole

stage is a blaze of light

The film P.R. notes

How by situation ...

The land of locktongue ··

scene photographers with

flash bulbs · organ musick ·

observe · distintegration

of Topaz : Photograph his

that Publicai a rally the

audience must cheer ·

when the packard is

shown

act 1 scene 1 hand of

lachaigne ·

several aspects · The picnic ·

Pyramidal · and geometric ·

when the audience arrives ·

Dream musick to a ready

marching for the beginning

The birthday is celebrated

with promises and the

gifts

Sitting watching the fire
ones mind turns outwards
not to a mythical childhood
nor a village idyll
nor to hope for any foreseable
                        future
but I suppose, like the wandering
Jew, it passes tableaux, these
in orange and emerald down
through the billboard promised
land.

    Where the lights talk and
offer consolation as well as shine
but chiefly the first, not being
primarily occupied with lighting
the way.

    And the city composed of
promises stretches outwards
into the night

and now the old poet sat by the lake
watching the ripples on the water
where the goldfish swam and
listening. for every now and then
where the young god had cast his golden
shadows. a word or a phrase
would escape in scintillating sparks
a poetry of fire. which cast the
whole place momentarily into
darkness with the brightness of its
reflections

     the heavens and earth are united
          in gold
     he combs (his hair)
     the golden rays
(in his hands) the roses burn
     the days are long
     the wheels turn in the circle
     cooled by breezes from the four corners
     he enters (his chamber)
     the swallow has risen (in the east)
     the doors are open.
    mankind is awakened.

     was now recorded

LARGER THAN LIFE:
A DECADE AND A BIT WITH
DEREK JARMAN

*

MICHAEL GINSBORG

DEREK JARMAN, NORTHWOOD, 1963.

I MET DEREK JARMAN IN THE AUTUMN of 1961 at King's College London. I was eighteen and the 1960s were definitely not swinging for me. I was a first-year medical student, which was the last thing in the world I wanted to be. Derek was taking a BA General degree. He already had a place at the Slade, and he had wanted to go there straight from school, but his father had insisted that he study for a degree first. There was a parallel with me, as my parents had insisted that I study medicine.

I had written poems and stories and had made drawings before going to King's. Derek, however, already had an established painting practice, having been encouraged by a remarkable art teacher at school. He had a studio in a neighbour's house in Northwood, Middlesex, where he was living with his parents. He made thick expressionist oil paintings of figures in interiors and landscapes, as well as charcoal drawings. He told me that the most important thing in painting, and the most difficult, was 'to keep the colours separate'. He worked consistently as an artist right through university. His degree course suited him, and he enjoyed it: History, History of Art and Architecture, English Literature. What was not to like?

Derek had the most extraordinary energy and an intense physical presence. He was very focused, totally committed to culture in the broadest sense and to his own practice. He would pick up on whatever was the latest thing, whether in music (of all kinds), film or exhibitions. Also, he was very photogenic. He knew this and liked posing for the camera, and there was usually someone around to capture the moment.

He never stopped. He charged off down the street, telling you facts about all the buildings and what he thought about them. He took great pleasure in pacing back and forth reciting Chaucer or Shakespeare. You might think that with this level of energy, this continuous fervour, he could have been impossible to be with. In fact, the opposite was true. He was social, warm and generous, always sharing his enthusiasms with others. In Derek's company you were participating in what Tony Peake described in his 1999 biography of Derek as 'the talk, the endless excited talk'.

During that year, Derek and I became close friends. For me at that time, a distracted, insecure teenager feeling like an outsider at medical school, meeting Derek turned out to be a life-changing encounter. The fact that he was not only immersed in art and literature academically but was making art as well was pivotal in my eventual decision to leave medicine altogether and go to art school.

During 1961 and 1962 we were both part of a group that worked on *Lucifer*, the King's termly literary review. Derek was the art editor. I contributed some poems and a short story; Derek, some ink drawings of a Greek island and a church interior. But it was Derek's cover for the autumn 1962 issue that surprised me the most. Onto the agonised figures of Adam and Eve in Masaccio's *Expulsion from the Garden of Eden*, Derek superimposed three brutal, near vertical black bands. What was the

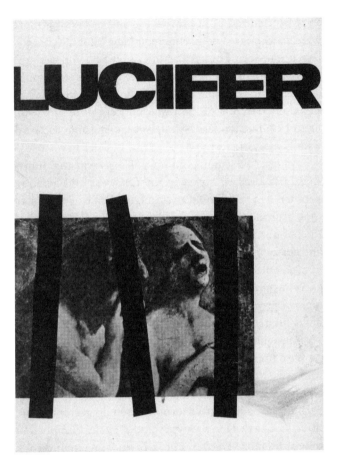

Lucifer COVER BY DEREK JARMAN, 1962.

suffering that he was referencing – or was he denying that suffering in some way? The Second World War had ended seventeen years previously, and in London there were many cleared bombsites reminding us of the conflict. Derek had seen Francis Bacon's paintings, and perhaps this had provoked him to reproduce this powerful image of the essential human condition. Possibly he wanted to signal his rejection of the whole concept of original sin, or to expunge his feelings of guilt as he came to terms with his sexuality.

Another welcoming group at King's was the drama society. I directed a play in my first year and acted in another. Anything to escape from medicine. The society took a production of Arthur Miller's *The Crucible* on a tour of northern Germany, and Derek designed the sets and costumes and doubled up as a kind of assistant stage manager, helping physically and dispensing wisdom and encouragement. We stayed with different families each night. Derek returned one morning in a disturbed state, angry that, in 1962, the house was still bedecked with Nazi insignia.

For the academic year of 1962–63, Derek's uncle found us a flat in a huge block called Witley Court, on Coram Street just north of Russell Square. By turning each of the rooms into bedrooms it could accommodate three students: Derek, myself and Dugald Campbell, a school friend of Derek's who was studying architecture. It was the first time that any of us had lived away from home. With an almost unnatural energy Derek set up his room (the largest) with significant objects that

DEREK JARMAN'S ROOM, WITLEY COURT, 1962.

he had collected. There was a substantial padded reading chair with a candleholder swivelling out from one arm and a lectern from the other. He brought with him a large paint-encrusted easel, a plentiful supply of art materials and a selection of canvases in progress. Two beautiful, tall wooden candlesticks that he had found in Rome completed the picture. The walls filled up with paintings. In the only photo I have of this room, a charcoal portrait of me hangs amidst his oil paintings. Music rang out from the stereo: Bach, Britten and lots of hypnotic Gregorian chant. This room was the first of Derek's 'stage set studios', combining workspace and social space. He created these as a kind of ongoing dialogue with himself and as a way to proclaim himself to his visitors. Dugald's and my rooms were monastic by comparison.

In the summer of 1963, we all left the flat. Derek went straight to the Slade, and I ended up at the Central School of Art and Design. Both were deeply conservative art schools, and Derek was not happy at the Slade. He wrote, in his fourth term, about the arts suffering from isolation within their respective disciplines. In his 'Tentative Ideas for a Manifesto', he stated: 'Theatre, ballet and painting must be revived. This cannot be achieved separately. There must be intercommunication.' He joined the Theatre Design course and immediately became much more engaged. Although he continued to paint until the end of his life, he realised as the 1960s wore on that painting could not do justice to the variety of ways in which he was interested in expressing himself.

Gradually he began to pursue his aspirations for a more inclusive, essentially visual, collaborative kind of artwork combining performance, narrative, music and the spoken word – a *Gesamtkunstwerk*, in other words, though I never heard him use that word. The tins of cheap Brodie & Middleton oil paint that he brought to Witley Court were no longer up to the job.

With hindsight, there was an inevitability about Derek becoming a filmmaker. I was inspired by his example to believe that I might become an artist – albeit an entirely different one from him.

By 1968, Derek was becoming better known, and much busier. His scenery and costume designs for *Jazz Calendar*, Frederick Ashton's ballet at the Royal Opera House, put him on the map once and for all. I was bowled over by the clarity, straightforward colour and elegant, abstract simplicity of the piece. It was a wonderful moment, and I admired Derek for having achieved it, much of the time against the odds.

In 1970, Derek and the artist Peter Logan moved into 51 Upper Ground, the first of their superb Thameside studio spaces. As at Witley Court, for Derek these were not simply workspaces but essentially social spaces as well. They served as theatrical backdrops for works in progress, and when necessary became collaborative workshop spaces. They were places where he could entertain, and even accommodate, his ever-growing group of friends and associates. Whether here or at Bankside later, when you went into his studio, there was always something new to see, some new discussion to be had.

DEREK JARMAN, UPPER GROUND, 1970.

The studios were also capable of acting as party venues. I was flattered to feature on the invitation to one huge party at Upper Ground. As one of the 'Plastic Fairies', I was photographed with my magic wand and in an immaculate white suit, seated between two beautiful young men, Herbert Muschamp and Karl Bowen. These were heady times. They were also highly creative times.

As Upper Ground faced demolition, Derek and Peter found another extraordinary premises, at 13 Bankside, next to Southwark Bridge. I joined them there in 1970, each of us with a separate vast studio space. Over the next two years I saw Derek on an almost daily basis, the first time since our student flat in 1963. A lot had happened in the intervening years, and by now we had all embarked on our professional paths. Derek was very happy. The river that 'glideth at his own sweet will' seemed to have a beneficent effect on us. Derek did his housework every Saturday morning, shaved every day in the improvised bathroom, and religiously ate his daily orange, which his mother had told him would ensure him good health. We ate in the cafés and pubs around Borough Market, and for a treat we drank wine in the evening at the Boot and Flogger on Borough High Street.

For Christmas 1970 we gave an enormous dinner party. Estimates of the number of guests vary between forty and fifty. We put up a very long table in Derek's studio. Derek and I sat at either end, in constant communication by walkie-talkie. We had bought a box of narcissi at Covent Garden and the room smelled wonderful, lit entirely by candles. We bought wine from Berry Bros. in St James's. Peter improvised a field kitchen in his studio and we ate watercress soup, turkey and Christmas pudding with brandy butter. Where did we get the money from? How did we find the time? I overheard one guest say, 'If this place goes up in flames tonight, half the London artworld will perish.' After dinner we played round after round of charades. The most spectacular entry, which was guessed immediately when the curtain was drawn back, was 'Rule Britannia'. With many guests acting as waves, Britannia was typecast, played by a formidable lady called Vera Russell.

Derek's career gathered momentum. He started working with Ken Russell through a chance encounter with a woman who knew the film director. Peake writes, 'Work would frequently come looking for Jarman, rather than the other way round.' He designed two films for Russell, the first, in 1971, being *The Devils*, for which I painted a copy of Poussin's *The Triumph of Pan*, which was cut to bits in the film by the soldiers who sacked Father Grandier's study. I was paid well for my work but I had hoped secretly to retain the painting. The second Russell film that Derek designed was *Savage Messiah* (1972), about the French sculptor Henri Gaudier-Brzeska. The numerous artefacts that were needed were produced in Derek's studio by students from Wimbledon School of Art, where I was teaching at the time. During the intensive pre-production periods for these films, Bankside became a hive of activity and film people were always coming and going. I had my own more than

DEREK JARMAN, UPPER GROUND, 1970.

adequate space, which was separate from the film stuff, save for a misunderstanding once when a production assistant assumed he could requisition it for Dorothy Tutin's wardrobe. I began to feel that I was caught up in Derek's slipstream.

In late 1971 I decided to leave Bankside. In January the following year I married Robby Nelson, an actress and a close friend of Derek's, whom I had met at King's a decade earlier. Derek was my best man. He wore a grey suit and took everything very seriously. We were all very happy and Derek was a tremendous support. It was a small wedding – just nine of us. Derek got on famously with everyone, as we drank champagne and whiled away the afternoon, unpicking the world and reassembling it, reminiscing and fantasising about our future plans.

DEREK JARMAN & DIANA GRACE JONES AT THE WEDDING
OF MICHAEL GINSBORG, JANUARY 1972.

AN AFTERWORD, IF YOU LIKE

*

DECLAN WIFFEN

IT SEEMS A CLICHÉ TO SAY THAT I first visited Dungeness after finding Jarman's *Smiling in Slow Motion* on a friend's bookshelf. Having read the posthumously published diaries, as well as *Modern Nature* (1991), I set off with two other queers in a rental car from Canterbury on a pilgrimage across Kent. For many of us who came to Jarman through his journals, Dungeness has become synonymous with his life and work. So it was only after my third or fourth listen to the audio version of *Through the Billboard Promised Land Without Ever Stopping* that I realised I had been picturing Jarman sitting at Prospect Cottage, reading the story into a cassette recorder, the pages of his typewritten copy close enough for us to hear him turning them. But this was just my imagination, because we have no knowledge of when, where or why the story was recorded. However, despite it being written in 1971, almost two decades before Jarman moved to Prospect Cottage, there is a faint haunting of Dungeness within the tale, which speaks to the strange fluidity of space and time the story embodies.

In an interview, Jarman said that Dungeness was 'very unusual and quite unlike anything I have seen in England ... Once one turns a corner into the Dungeness road, one is in another world.'[1] This is similarly true of turning the page into *Through the Billboard Promised Land Without Ever Stopping*, where we find ourselves in the other world of surreal America – Jarman having started writing the story shortly after returning from the United States – as the King and John travel past huge signs with flashing messages, adverts in crystal and chrome, and screens on silver wires showing movies. With its filmic imagery and cinematic descriptions, it might seem inevitable that the world of film would be where Jarman ended up. But like the travellers who are told by the Begum in flowered chintzes that they are at 'the last outpost of Movietown', we know that Jarman ended up not in Hollywood but at the final frontier on the southern coastline of England.

In the same interview, he went on to make a direct link between the landscape of Dungeness and that of the Billboard Promised Land, saying, 'In some ways [Dungeness] reminded me of North America, with its telegraph poles and crazy angles.'[2] And later, he wrote that at night the nuclear power station behind his cottage was like 'a small Manhattan ablaze with a thousand lights of different colours'.[3] Although worlds apart, the commingling of America with Dungeness speaks to the out-of-jointness of Jarman's creative practice, one that did not adhere to strict laws of time and space, or expectation.

As his only known work of short fiction, *Through the Billboard Promised Land Without Ever Stopping* is an anomaly in Jarman's creative practice, adding another artistic form to his long list of experiments and accomplishments. But in another sense, the story's aesthetic and content connect threads that run across his oeuvre. It was revised numerous times, sharing parallels with Jarman's wider practice as an artist, as does its inclusion of various symbols, leitmotifs and refrains that appear throughout his work. The story's relation to practices of collage signals his preference for recycling material over any

glitz or glamour of 'the new' offered by the commodification and consumerism of the Billboard Promised Land.
Displaying both the clear influence of and a resistance to
American cultural traditions, the story contributes to an
understanding of why Jarman rejected Hollywood and
instead focused on low-budget experimental art films
in Europe. Written in the same year he made his first
film, *Electric Fairy*, the narrative style gives clues as to
the development of his filmic sensibility and an insight
into his creative process. And, while being less overtly
political than much of Jarman's later work, the story is
an inchoate exploration of intimacy between two male
companions that rejects the temporality and idea of
progress so aligned with heteronormative society.

A process of revision and reinvention,
without ever stopping

In Jarman's papers, held at the BFI Archive, the text
appears in various forms but has never before been available to a wider audience. When researching the story
back in 2018, the sole reference to it I could find was in
Tony Peake's definitive biography of Jarman, the only
reason I knew about the story's existence in the first
place. Peake writes that 'Through the billboard promised
land' was one of Jarman's favourite phrases, coined on
his first trip to North America in 1964, which inspired
much of his only book of poetry, *A Finger in the Fishes
Mouth*.[4] The refrain is repeated throughout the 1972
collection in 'Poem for Coleridge July 64', 'Poem

VII Farewell', and again in 'From Gypsy Mar 1 66',
which reads:

> I had a dream
> in the dawn light
> the clouds reflecting the fire of the billboard
>   promised land
> stalking the violet sky
> floating the highways of delight[5]

It also appears, in Jarman's distinctive cursive scrawl, on
the mirrored back cover of the book, spelt there 'Thru',
the contraction giving further indication of America's influence on the phrase. Upon returning to London, Jarman
began making notes for a play centred around 'the land
of Cockaigne', but after a brief attempt he writes 'Jettison
the pages before' and starts afresh. Following this, in the
winter of 1965, a new notebook includes a version of
the play, called simply 'The Billboard Promised Land'.[6]
Falling somewhere between *The Wizard of Oz* and *Alice
in Wonderland*, it exists in multiple forms and drafts,
some versions naming the wandering king 'Ludwig of
Bavaria'. When Tariq Ali offered him the opportunity to
make a film about the philosopher Ludwig Wittgenstein
in the early 1990s, Jarman was reported to have said,
'I've always wanted to make a film called *Mad Ludwig*',[7]
a reference to a lost iteration of the wandering King and
an indication that the story was still circling in Jarman's
mind. After the second variation of the play, he returned to work on a short story of the same title in 1971,

before the title was augmented to 'My journey through the billboard promised land without ever stopping if you like with John and Amethyst the King'. The latter half of this title gets scored out in his handwritten journal, and a blue pen scribbles over 'My Journey' in one of the typed copies, so that we are left with *Through the Billboard Promised Land Without Ever Stopping*.

The variations of title, characters and events in the story are indicative of Jarman's approach to creative practice more generally. For example, it chimes with this description of the way *Kicking the Pricks* (1987) is said to have been written:

> Derek extensively re-edited and re-ordered the text, scrubbing out the past, inverting meanings, ruthlessly cutting so that pages were returned bleeding from their red Pentel duels – a process of revision and re-invention that was characteristic in his painting, writing, film editing, and personal history.[8]

The ideas within the short story kept circling back, and Jarman elaborated them in different ways at different times. In this sense, *Through the Billboard Promised Land Without Ever Stopping* is a work that was itself never stopping, constantly evolving, rather than a finished product. The version published here is a transcript of an audio recording in which Jarman reads the story and, as if unable to allow the text to become finalised, he changes the title again to 'Through the Billboard Promised Land Without Ever Stopping, if You Like', confirming the fluidity of his approach. The choice not to include this last clause in the published title was taken after assessing the consistency of titles used in archival versions of the story, the final draft of which this transcript correlates with very closely and against which some formatting decisions have been made. There are one or two things that Jarman seems to have rephrased in the audio version, plus a few additional sentences here and there. The only major difference is the ordering of the latter half of the story, after John and the King leave the court of the Yellow Empress. In the final archive draft, the boys struggling in the water and the avenue of broken statues appear immediately, whereas in the audio version they have been moved until later on, adding a building sense of the apocalyptic. The audio version was passed on to Tony Peake by Keith Collins – H.B., Jarman's long-term partner – with whom House Sparrow Press publishers Jess Chandler and Gareth Evans discussed publication of the story before his death in 2018.

'Narrative is the first trap'

Through the Billboard Promised Land Without Ever Stopping has the narrative drive of a camp and surreal road-trip movie, in which the protagonists journey from place to place, encountering a host of characters and situations along the way, much like Jarman's favourite film, *The Wizard of Oz* (1939). However, it is not quite as straightforward as that film, for the desires and motivations of the characters are less apparent than those of Dorothy and her friends. While this story may not go quite as far as having a 'principle of non-narration',[9] as has been said of Jarman's films, disruptions to traditional narrative occur in a variety of ways such that it resonates with Jarman's invitation to the audience in his last film, *Blue* (1993), to 'fight the fear that engenders the beginning, the middle and the end'.[10] Jarman was to say later that 'Narrative is the first trap of commercial cinema', and the story gives early indications of this resistance to conventional storytelling.[11]

The story begins somewhat *in media res*, with no details as to the background of the characters and only a hazy sense of motivation as to why they leave Fargo. The sequence of events has almost no relation to cause and effect, and the final paragraph of the story offers various rumours about ways the tale ends. The scenes can also be said to come and go too quickly, shifting from Movietown to the strawberry beds of the eternal present, from the city of Disc to a landscape where pyramids rise out of a snowy plane. This narrative movement can leave the reader perplexed and wanting more. It is similar to the effect described by Peter Fillingham of watching Jarman's 1975 short film *Sebastian Wrap*: 'Just at the point of understanding, of grasping the image … of fixing a time and a narrative, the image disappears and I want it back.'[12]

Jarman's story offers us a looser, dreamlike relation to narrative, following the example set by the Beat poets, who did not prioritise simple causality, mimesis or the fetishising of intelligibility. While less obscene, the story also betrays the influence of William Burroughs's *Naked Lunch* (1959), another road trip across a surreal America, structured in vignettes that Burroughs claimed could be read in any order.[13] Even Jarman's account of buying *Naked Lunch* bears a similar fluidity to his approach of writing this story, telling us in *Dancing Ledge* (1984) that he bought it while visiting a lover in Canada, and then in *At Your Own Risk* (1992) recounting that he purchased it from the City Lights bookstore in San Francisco.

Through the Billboard Promised Land Without Ever Stopping employs a similar, if less overt, technique of construction whereby the montage of scenes the two characters travel through is collated in a manner that gives an insight into the development of his artistic practice. The narrative movement through the Billboard Promised Land is antithetical to the straightness of the Superhighway, a single road in two directions. Instead, Jarman's narrative takes us on a series of detours off the Superhighway in an arrangement of scenes that could quite easily be shuffled and reordered with little detriment to the tale. As Peake writes, 'there is a telling aimlessness about the journey, a sense that the sequence of its events is without true purpose.'[14] But the characters could be said to be following an alternative agenda, travelling their own 'highways of delight'.

Alexandra Parsons has written extensively about Jarman's use of collage as a queer activist practice, particularly in his life-writing, a method that enables Jarman to form 'new registers for living'.[15] Collaging scraps of text, images and ideas from various places can be understood as a queer modality for its method of undermining stable identities, celebrating hybrid lineages and reinterpreting found material.[16] Jarman favours a fluid approach to self-fashioning that allows for multiplicity, rejecting memory as concrete, history as singular and reality as objective. In a culture that was not only increasingly commercial and scarcely funded but also suffocated by what became state-sanctioned homophobia under Margaret Thatcher, Jarman rejects linearity, progress and the fetishisation of origins that dominate what he termed 'Heterosoc'. He chose instead to embrace a queerer relation to time and place, allowing the trajectory of his life and art to take an alternative path to that expected.

The story embodies this deviation from a singular truth. Like the landscape of *The Garden* (1990), which is a symbol of both Eden and Gethsemane, the Billboard Promised Land presents readers with a world of contrasts in a pandemonium of images. Out in this world of paradox, a blind and beautiful King sets off with John, his valet, on a 'journey with no destination' or conclusion. They leave the domestic space of the villa, one that is 'perfectly comfortable' but has an air of stasis: 'the lawns are green, and nothing ever changes'. Instead, they choose to set off into the unknown, announcing: 'We will turn our backs to the sun, and walk into the dark. That is the signpost we shall follow.' On the one hand, the landscape they travel is psychedelic and full of luminous colour, from sodium lamps and pink neon trees to glowing mesembryanthemums and phosphorescent sea creatures. But on the other, it is a world where 'night [has] been turned into day' and 'colour has deserted the world'. There is an air of excitement and desire leading them onwards, while death and destruction haunt their path.

A wholehearted love affair with the American Dream?

The multiplicity of, and ambivalence towards, the Billboard Promised Land highlights Jarman's complicated relationship with America. He described his youthful intrigue with the country as a consequence of growing up in post-war Britain under the influence of an America that was impossible to evade:

in the 1950s we dreamed the American dream. England was grey and sober. The war had retrenched all the virtues – Sobriety and Thrift came with the Beveridge plan, utility furniture, and rationing, which lasted about a decade after the end of hostilities. Over the Atlantic lay the land of cockaigne; they had fridges and cars, TV and supermarkets. All bigger and better than ours. Food parcels arrived with unheard-of luxuries: bubble-gum and chocolate, fruit cakes wrapped in comics – all virtually unobtainable here. Then, as the decade wore on, we were sent Presley and Buddy Holly, and long-playing records of *West Side Story*, and our own *Pygmalion* transformed. The whole daydream was wrapped up in celluloid, and presented nightly at the 'Odious' at the end of every high street in the land. How we yearned for America! And longed to go west. In 1960 every young English artist had an eye across the Atlantic.[17]

Jarman left for North America in the summer of 1964, first visiting 'screaming manhattan', where he rode 'subways at 100mph', saw 'serpent taxis … winding through stainless steel corsets' and wandered the Lower East Side listening to 'Europe's distracted sons … singing a new world song'.[18] America was full of promises, from sexual liberation to the fusion of the social and the political. But instead of diving into this freedom, he resisted the advances of a gang of randy priests, not yet ready to sing his own new sexual song. He wanted sexual freedom, but he had come to the New World because of a man he had met earlier that year in London, Ron Wright. Hopping on the long Greyhound to Canada, the two shared a basement flat in Calgary for the summer, a time spent together that Jarman describes as idyllic:

> We spent nearly all our spare time in the countryside, sitting sunning ourselves on huge flat glacial rocks, spread along the icy sparkling rivers which rushed down from the Rockies, or climbed the mountains.[19]

But as Peake suggests, Jarman tended to put a 'jaunty gloss on his first transatlantic trip',[20] including memories of his first love. It is not until 1992, in *At Your Own Risk*, that the repeated anecdote of this trip includes details of a more tempestuous nature, Jarman admitting that the two argued and as 'the rows got worse I took off for San Francisco'.[21] On the West Coast he hung around the City Lights bookstore, another of the main draws for his trip, later picking up a joint-rolling biker, writing poetry while high, seeing Joan Baez and Bob Dylan perform, and having other intimate encounters with men.

Although some of the details are hazy and retold differently across Jarman's writings, what is clear is that the time he spent travelling in North America changed Jarman, and not only via his erotic awakening. His sexually repressed past 'broke up like ice in a spring thaw',[22] as did his faithfulness to the old England that had produced him, even if America's brashness and fixation on 'the new' did not sit with his disposition. If his contemporary David Hockney was 'in a wholehearted love affair with the American Dream'[23] then Jarman maintained a distance and scepticism of America alongside his youthful intrigue. This becomes more apparent when, back at the Slade as an art student, he derides the dismantling of the antique room a year after he returned from his travels,[24] writing scathingly that 'the Renaissance had at last succumbed to the air-conditioned nightmare of Pop'. His distaste for America seeped out in his proposed design work for Stravinsky's *Orpheus*, where 'the gates of hell are the Brooklyn Bridge. This unconsciously delineated my attitude to "American" Popism, nicely.'[25]

Jarman chose to stay in England and work on smaller, collaborative projects, rather than make moves for a career in Hollywood. He had worked on Ken Russell's large-scale film *The Devils* (1971), after which Jarman's agent tried to persuade him to pursue more work in Los Angeles, but he turned down further offers to work on design and costume for big-budget films with Russell, and then Stanley Kubrick, deciding that the financial impetus was not worth the energy and time that took him away from his own artistic practice. Perhaps more importantly, he didn't believe it would be possible to preserve his identity as a gay man if he gave himself over to commercial cinema.[26]

Luminous and opaque: the poetry of fire

Instead, in the same year as Jarman reworked 'The Billboard Promised Land' into a short story, he made his first film. *Electric Fairy* was made on 16mm and had been thought lost until it was discovered by Jarman's producer James Mackay in 2008. *Electric Fairy* depicts a curly-haired man in large headphones sitting in front of a plastic backdrop covered in butterflies and planets. Bubbles flow over him before he watches a caterpillar crawl over two porcelain figures on a large pumpkin, and then dances with the creature before popping it in his mouth. Of this earliest film's creation, Peake writes that Malcolm Leigh tried to explain to Jarman that 'a film needs a story', but Jarman wasn't interested, favouring a disjointed montage. This approach chimes with Mackay's comments that *Electric Fairy* 'fits in precisely with the slightly later films on Super 8 … [setting] the style and direction of Derek's future works'.[27]

The development and creation of Jarman's first Super 8s are detailed in *Dancing Ledge* alongside two sections of *Through the Billboard Promised Land*, bringing together the development and influence of each medium on the other. Cut and pasted alongside fragments of memory from different time periods, this method of representation is similar in practice to the construction of his poetic voice, in which 'time and history are conceived of as a palimpsest'.[28] This layering of memories alongside the story includes the making of *The Art of Mirrors*, a short film of 1973 in which sunlight is reflected into the camera lens. Jarman writes that 'This is the first film we've made on Super 8 in which there is nothing to compare … At last we have something completely new',[29] bringing the story into connection with this new phase of creativity.

Additionally, he tells of discovering Carl Jung's *Alchemical Studies* and *Seven Sermons to the Dead*, which gave him the permission and 'the confidence to allow my dream-images to drift and collide at random'[30] without having to meet the expectations of the subsidised avant-garde, who didn't take his work seriously. Evoking Jung in this context begins to help form a constellation of Jarman's own approach: a trust in the unconscious, a belief in the symbolic nature of images, a commitment to a shifting and magical aesthetic. Collaging this memory alongside *Through the Billboard Promised Land* gives a sense of the ways in which the story is formed as Jarman's experimental film projects were also developing.

John and the King's travels, switching between geography and atmosphere as they do, show a certain confluence between Jarman's writing style and the emergence of his interest in film. Both resist linearity, collide the modern and the ancient, embrace obscurity and enjoy the dream-like confusion that entangling such ideas produces.

In fact, Jarman goes on to explicitly link the way film and writing are connected for him:

> This is the way the Super 8s are structured from writing: the buried word-signs emphasize the fact that they convey a language. There is the image and the word, and the image of the word. The 'poetry of fire' relies on a treatment of word and object as equivalent: both are signs; both are luminous and opaque. The pleasure of Super 8s is the pleasure of seeing language put through the magic lantern.[31]

'The poetry of fire' is a phrase that occurs in *Through the Billboard Promised Land* – as well as *Blue* (1993) – to describe the moment the sun god, Helios, gets lost in the mirrored labyrinth that protects the entrance to the city of Disc. Helios becomes 'maddened by his own burning and distorted reflections' and falls into the lake, casting 'the whole place momentarily into darkness with the brightness of its reflections'. There is a striking affinity here with the techniques used in *The Art of Mirrors*, where Jarman reflects the sun into the lens, 'sending the whole film lurching into negative',[32] as well as *In the Shadow of the Sun* (1981), where fire mazes are used in various shots, superimposed and repeated, and *Electric Fairy*, where a red neon bulb fills the frame and becomes blurred.

In relation to the difficulty of finding meaning in Jarman's experimental cinema, Christopher Hauke suggests that audiences too often focus on 'looking for signs, rather than taking in the symbols'. He goes on to inform us that in Jungian psychoanalysis 'a sign points to something already known while a symbol refers to something unknown that, as yet, cannot be expressed in any other way'.[33] Jarman's encouragement to think of 'word and object as equivalent ... luminous and opaque' shifts our expectation of language as a communicator of fixed truths to a more indeterminate mode of expression. Language becomes an image-symbol of the as yet unknown. This makes it possible to grasp something of the poetic and filmic quality of his writing when thought of as similar to his creation of images. In the story, when the poet bends over the water listening for phrases that might escape the pool, the images that follow are rather poetic. When the earlier version of this passage is included in *Dancing Ledge*, it is longer and resembles a list of frames, similar to those Jarman wrote in notebooks when planning his shoots:

> The heaven and earth are united in gold
> he combs (his hair)
> the golden rays
> (in his hands) the roses burn
> the days are long
> the wheel turns in the circle

cooled by breezes from the four corners
he enters (his chamber)
the swallow has risen (in the east)
the doors are open
man awakes[34]

The text's separation into lines invites us to focus on small individual moments, breaking the prose into what looks like a poem. It is but a small step to imagine these words become images in the style of a Super 8 film, where a shot of 'a butterfly trapped in a glass' shifts into one of 'wind on the sea'.

As his filmmaking developed, superimposition, colour gels, montage, playing with the speed of projection and re-filming of images all began to work together to layer time and place in a single shot, disorienting linear narrative and embracing the ambiguity and indeterminacy of meaning. Although there is no neat way to map these onto prose, the collaging, reworking and drift between scenes in *Through the Billboard Promised Land* suggests a strong correlation between the different modes of Jarman's artistic practices.

A funny habit of repeating

As already mentioned, Jarman had a habit of revisiting imagery, retelling stories and recycling material across different mediums. *Through the Billboard Promised Land* is an early example of this, and contains many connections to other projects, so much so that Peake writes that it acts like a 'checklist of images and phrases central to his paintings and, later, his films'[35] – to which I would add his writing.

The path along which a white cat leads John and the King is lined with fragments of marble torsos. They pass by heads whose 'huge, unseeing eyes' and 'locks of stone hair permed forever' recall the bust of Mausolus that Jarman recast when the Slade closed its antique room. The head can be seen in various films, including *Jubilee* (1978) and *The Tempest* (1979), and now resides inside Prospect Cottage. Two mixed-media collages from the 1970s, *The Fragments of Antiquity* (c.1975) and *Pleasures of Italy* (c.1979), also have statues 'piled one on top of another like used cars in a breaker's yard'.[36] This leitmotif, introduced in this story, demonstrates the fracturing yet persistent presence of classical culture scattered across Jarman's work.

Another early symbol that Jarman used time and again appears in the story's opening, where a swallow flies into the King's bedroom and circles three times before leaving. It perhaps represents a freedom of movement that encourages the King to set off on his convoluted journey, darting between scenes like the flight of the bird. Jarman writes in his journal that 'Childhood memories have a funny habit of repeating',[37] and the origin of the swallow as motif can be traced back to his time in Italy, where at 'Four years old … A swallow sweeps in through the window along a random sunbeam like a dark meteorite through galaxies of glowing dust clouds. *Itys itys itys.*'[38] It is used later in *Caravaggio* (1986), just after the artist has died, when the voice-over of a young Michele (a version of Jarman?) narrates a very similar account of the bird flying 'along the beam and landing with its wings spread, black as a crucifix on the wall'.[39] This repetition contains the imagery of death that also accompanies Jarman's telling of his mother's passing, at which he and his sister held on to her hands 'as her life fluttered away like the proverbial swallows'.[40] Finally, the birds become part of daily life in summer down at Dungeness, where he sits watching them, writing on Monday 18 June 1991: 'It is silent and deserted here, just myself and the swallows.'[41] The combination of freedom, death and companionship in this repeated image attests to the shifting, unstable and heterogeneous meanings that infuse Jarman's work.

Other significant instances of recycling include the Begum in flowered chintzes, who makes an appearance in *A Finger in the Fishes Mouth*, as do various images, such as pages of newspaper blown in the wind, a man with violets in his eyes, and the 'lawns of eternal rest'. Similarly, 'The road to the city of Aqua Vitae … protected by a labyrinth' reappears at the end of *Blue*, where the same archaeologists listen for fragments of the past by a blue lake, which itself is reminiscent of Jarman's painting *Landscape with Blue Pool* from 1967. Finally, the refrain 'Due to lack of interest, tomorrow has been cancelled' is repeated in *The Last of England* (1987), itself magpied from Irene Kampen's 1969 book; and Borgia Ginz, the host at the Temple of Autodestruction, reappears in *Jubilee* as a media mogul, a character 'whose name, if not aspect' Peake suggests 'is a reference to Jarman's former flatmate from Witley Court, Michael Ginsborg', who is also a contributor to this book.[42]

There are undoubtedly more crossovers and entanglements to be explored, but what is manifest from those detailed here is Jarman's recycling, reuse and reinvention of material across his different artistic practices. He chose to convert and repurpose scraps of his work in an aesthetic practice that refused the consumerism and commodification promised by the billboard culture of the USA. At one point in the story, the two travellers see a mountain built out of offerings that people have carried on their backs: 'cars and refrigerators and television sets, countless objects of plastic, and motorbikes'. The surreal setting is fused with reality, a place where waste is tossed away, creating a junkyard Babel stretching up to the sky. Jarman critiques the 'god' of capitalism who requires sacrifices of cheap commodities, and links it to the environmental destruction that also haunts the landscape. In Movietown, 'Flowers and trees no longer grew', and where the deathly 'funereal cypress trees' are able to grow, they stand in a landscape where no lizards scuttle or flies buzz. Jarman's concern for the climate and his repurposing of debris are seen here to link back to some of his earliest artistic work.

The world of reflections broken into pieces

Through the Billboard Promised Land Without Ever Stopping doesn't contain the confronting politics present in much of Jarman's other work. However, it does offer an inchoate exploration of intimacy between two male companions, whose journey away from the stasis of domesticity is a rejection of the ideas of progress, temporality and worth so aligned with heteronormative society. Although influenced by the Beat poets, this work is no Ginsbergian portrayal of sexuality, with its cocks and assholes and BDSM – they were to come later, in *Sebastiane* (1976), *The Garden* and *Modern Nature* (1991). Rather, we get brief moments of affection between the King and John that show a nascent desire for closeness and friendship between men.

We see snippets of this before leaving the villa when the two men walk arm in arm down to the swimming pool, where they bathe together, and when, on their journey, John reaches out to touch the King's forehead with water and later kisses him while he sleeps. These small, simple gestures of tenderness almost get lost in the buzz and speed of the wider story. But Jarman gives us a small clue to look out for them in a comment he made to his friend Dom Sylvester Houédard, to whom he nervously showed the story, saying, 'this is by the way autobiographical although deeply buried'.[43] If there are traces of Jarman's life in the story, they have gone through the rebus-like dreamwork of condensation and displacement in the writing process, such that the narrative is surreal and often bizarre. Yet, as in dreams, there are traces of real life, some of which can be connected to those Jarman narrated elsewhere.

One example of this is the moment when John looks into the King's sparkling eyes and a girl sings, 'in the common silence of this world, the white poppies of my love are dancing'. The same refrain is found in 'Poem 1', which is positioned as the third to last text of *A Finger in the Fishes Mouth*, adding a sense of closure to the lines.

Dancing Ledge sheds further light on the poem's origin, connecting it specifically to a memory of Ron. Outside the windows of the basement flat in Calgary, 'Ron's Russian neighbours cultivated opium poppies which they picked every morning to make their opium tea.'[44] Jarman ends the section where he decides to leave for San Francisco by pasting the poem at the end of this memory. The poppies symbolise an intoxicating yet fragile beauty, and the lines contain a sense of finitude, as if Jarman knew that, despite Ron promising to visit England again the next spring, he was saying goodbye to his first love. The refrain's presence in the story, sung by a third party, recalls this relationship, as the two characters float in the air, gazing into each other's eyes, before John catches the King in his arms.

A further suggestion that the King could be read as Jarman and John as Ron is found in Ron's memories of what it was like to spend time with Jarman and the differences in their backgrounds and social class. We might well ask, why a King and a valet? Ron recounted that he and Jarman were opposites:

I was very much from 'nowhere,' but this is very romanticized in Europe … and [Derek's] from a very aristocratic background. He's very, very much from 'somewhere' so I learned a lot from Derek and I'm very grateful.[45]

This social distinction is replicated in the story, as is the King's desire to be led by John out of the comfort of what he knows. Again, this chimes with Jarman's recollection of meeting Ron:

> After I switched the lights off I lay in the dark with my heart pounding. Then Ron said, 'Why don't you come over to my bed, it's really cold in here.' I nearly fell over in the haste with which I crossed the room – in case he changed his mind. I leapt into his bed. Each time I touched him it was like an electric shock.[46]

Along with leading Jarman into a new experience of intimacy, Ron certainly took him beyond his comfort zone. When he heard nothing from Ron following their evening's closeness, 'some dark force overwhelmed' him and he began slashing his own paintings with a knife.[47] The volatility of this relationship and the rows they went on to have are not detailed in the story, although we may glimpse something of this dynamic when the characters are disturbed by two others:

> John dipped his fingers in [the water] and touched Amethyst the King's forehead. Suddenly the quiet was interrupted, two boys were struggling in the water, the peaceful world of reflections swayed and broke into pieces as they fought.

The boys are a mirror image of the King and John, which could suggest that they are also Jarman and his lover, the names Ron and John being not too far apart to make something of. But we may want to resist the lure of bio-graphical fallacy because, just as the fighting boys break the world of reflections into pieces, Jarman's writing simi-larly fractures any sense of direct relation back to reality.

Intimacy in a wilderness of failure

At an event in 2014 to celebrate the publication of the facsimile edition of *A Finger in the Fishes Mouth*, Keith Collins told an anecdote that I feel is a synecdoche of much about this short story. Commenting on a passage he was about to read, he said:

> It was originally an old love letter Derek sent to me … subsequently it was used in *Modern Nature* and the film *The Garden*, and somehow I'm wondering whether it was recycled for me and other people had seen it beforehand. I was charmed at the time … maybe it wasn't quite as original as I thought.[48]

Collins recounted the tale in such a way as to make the audience laugh, and went on to read the following:

> I want to share this emptiness with you. Not fill the silence with false notes or put tracks through the void. I want to share this wilderness of failure. The others have built you a highway – fast lanes in both directions. I offer you a journey without direction, uncertainty and no sweet conclusion.

When the light faded, I went in search of myself.

There were many paths and many destinations.

This passage mirrors the desire of *Through the Billboard Promised Land Without Ever Stopping*: to share intimacy without dogma in a world heading towards destruction. At Prospect Cottage, where Jarman moved shortly after his HIV diagnosis, he shared his time with many companions down on the south Kent coast, in relations and friendships queerer than any labels might conjure.

In the story, when the King asks, 'Can you hear the sea in the roar of the surf on the shingles embracing the earth?' there are again untimely echoes of Jarman's life at Dungeness. I want to respond by saying, 'Yes, I can hear', in part because I have visited his garden and sat listening to the stones tumble as the waves lap the shore. But mostly because Jarman's cinematic prose ushers us into a readerly intimacy such that it is difficult not to feel addressed by the King's questions: 'Are you here in the springtime by the sea with me, John?' Reading this story, we all become Jarman's travelling companions across the Billboard Promised Land, we who have set off with him, in one way or another, in search of ourselves, and learned from him that there are many paths and many destinations, but no sweet conclusions.

1. 'Gardener's Question Time: Derek Jarman', interview, *The Garden* press materials, 1990, available at https://metrograph.com/gardeners-question-time-derek-jarman, accessed 10 August 2022.

2. Ibid.

3. Derek Jarman, *Derek Jarman's Garden* (London: Thames & Hudson, 1995), p. 67.

4. Tony Peake, *Derek Jarman* (London: Abacus, 1996), p. 170.

5. Derek Jarman, 'From Gypsy Mar 1 66', in *A Finger in the Fishes Mouth* (Bettiscombe, Dorset: Bettiscombe Press, 1972; repr. London: Test Centre, 2014), Poem 3.

6. Derek Jarman Special Collection, BFI National Archive, Box 49, Item 3.

7. Peake, *Derek Jarman*, p. 556, n. 68.

8. Keith Collins, 'Preface', in Derek Jarman, *Kicking the Pricks* [1987] (London: Vintage, 1996).

9. Tracy Biga, 'The Principle of Non-Narration in the Films of Derek Jarman', in *By Angels Driven: The Films of Derek Jarman*, ed. Chris Lippard (Trowbridge, Wilts: Flicks Books, 1996), p. 12.

10. Derek Jarman, *Chroma* (London: Century, 1994; repr. London: Vintage, 2019), p. 91.

11. Peake, *Derek Jarman*, p. 326.

12. Peter Fillingham, 'Beyond Language: At the Seams of Seduction', in James Mackay, ed., *Derek Jarman Super 8* (London: Thames & Hudson, 2014), pp. 172–76.

13. Michael Charlesworth reminds us that Jarman was writing around the time when English experimental writer B. S. Johnson's *The Unfortunates* (1969) was published, a 'book in a box' that came unbound in 27 sections to be shuffled and reordered at the reader's will. Michael Charlesworth, *Derek Jarman* (London: Reaktion Books, 2011), p. 52.

14. Peake, *Derek Jarman*, p. 171.

15. Alexandra Parsons, *Luminous Presence: Derek Jarman's Life Writing* (Manchester: Manchester University Press, 2022), p. 17.

16. For further ideas on collage as a queer medium, see Jack Halberstam, *The Queer Art of Failure* (Durham, NC: Duke University Press, 2011); Daniel Fountain, 'Hannah Höch and the Queer Art of Collage', *Collage Research Network Blog*, June 2019, https://collageresearchnetwork.wordpress.com/2019/06/13/the-art-of-hannah-hoch-queering-collage-via-jack-halberstam, accessed 10 August 2022.

17. Derek Jarman, *Dancing Ledge* (London: Quartet, 1984; repr. London: Vintage, 2022), p. 41.

18. Derek Jarman, 'Manhattan', in *A Finger in the Fishes Mouth*, Poem 23.

19. Jarman, *Dancing Ledge*, p. 44.

20. Peake, *Derek Jarman*, p. 99.

21. Derek Jarman, *At Your Own Risk: A Saint's Testament* (London: Hutchinson, 1992; repr. London: Vintage, 1993), p. 49.

22. Jarman, *Dancing Ledge*, p. 48.

23. Ibid., p. 64.

24. The Antique Room contained various plaster casts taken from classical sculptures that were used as teaching tools for the students at the Slade.

25. Jarman, *Dancing Ledge*, p. 89.

26. Peake, *Derek Jarman*, p. 170

27. James Mackay, notes on *Electric Fairy*, 2020, https://amandawilkinsongallery.com/artists/31-derek-jarman/works/7070-derek-jarman-electric-fairy-1971, accessed 10 August 2022.

28. Parsons, *Luminous Presence*, p. 32.

29. Jarman, *Dancing Ledge*, p. 91.

30. Ibid., p. 92.

31. Ibid., p. 94.

32. Ibid., p. 91.

33. Christopher Hauke, '"A Cinema of Small Gestures": Derek Jarman's Super 8 – Image, Alchemy, Individuation', *International Journal of Jungian Studies*, 6/2 (2014), pp. 159–64.

34. Jarman, *Dancing Ledge*, p. 91.

35. Peake, *Derek Jarman*, p. 171.

36. Jarman, *Dancing Ledge*, p. 94.

37. Derek Jarman, *Modern Nature* (London: Century, 1991; repr. London: Vintage, 2018), p. 18.

38. Jarman, *Dancing Ledge*, p. 5.

39. Derek Jarman, *Derek Jarman's 'Caravaggio'* (London: Thames & Hudson, 1986), p. 94.

40. Jarman, *Dancing Ledge*, p. 130.

41. Jarman, *Modern Nature*, p. 295.

42. Peake, *Derek Jarman*, p. 111.

43. Peake, *Derek Jarman*, p. 171.

44. Jarman, *Dancing Ledge*, p. 44.

45. Ron Wright, *Foretellings: A Life History,* ed. Jeff Friedman (San Francisco: GLBT Historical Society, 1994), p. 9.

46. Jarman, *Dancing Ledge*, p. 42.

47. Ibid.

48. Keith Collins in *A Finger in the Fishes Mouth: The Legacy of Derek Jarman*, LRB podcast, 19 February 2014, www.londonreviewbookshop.co.uk/podcasts-video/podcasts/a-finger-in-the-fishes-mouth-the-legacy-of-derek-jarman, accessed 10 August 2022. It appears that the quote is not from *Modern Nature*.

TELL IT IN BREAKING ENGLAND:
DEREK JARMAN'S
PERSISTENCE OF VISION

*

GARETH EVANS

THERE ARE SOME LINES BY BRECHT, from his poem 'To Those Born Later', written back in the pit of 1940, that are quoted more and more often now: 'What kind of times are these when / To talk about trees is almost a crime / Because it implies silence about so many horrors?' Indeed, and still true, but with a major caveat – now many of the horrors are happening also to the trees, and what strikes them makes our own plight so much the worse.

In bleak periods, some people say that art (define it how you wish) doesn't matter. How can it, when compared to the lack of bread, heat, shelter? A false opposition, of course: those people have rarely experienced hardship. If they had, they would know that art matters the most precisely when everything beneath one's feet is shaking. Out on the frayed edges of life, the fact of knowing that some have imagined both such scenarios *and* other worlds – of joy, coexistence, fecund and unfettered realms of collaborative being – is exactly what enables the enduring, the coming through.

Derek Jarman was canonised by gay male nuns the Sisters of Perpetual Indulgence on 22 September 1991. He described it as one of the most important events in his life. Now, more than 30 years later, he has become part of England's cultural canon, a 'national treasure'. That a radically queer, activist artist with a hugely prolific cross-disciplinary body of work can join such a lineage is both exhilarating and a warning. It shows how much the 'Overton window' of acceptance has broadened, but runs the risk of a dilution, a soundbite softening of Jarman's extraordinary artistic, political, sexual and social resonance, and relevance.

That is not to say that events marking his expanded status are without merit – far from it. Already this year, in what would have been Jarman's 80th, we have seen major exhibitions and their attendant finely produced catalogues (*Protest!* curated by Fiona Corridan and Jon Savage at Manchester Art Gallery, and *Modern Nature* curated by Philip Hoare with John Hansard Gallery), retrospective film programmes, shows internationally, and the publication of *Pharmacopoeia* (Vintage Classics), a carefully assembled 'book of days', highlighting his writing on nature and gardening with the 'white space' devotion accorded to Zen koans or the many aphoristic volumes of philosophically sourced self-improvement. In authentic and significant ways, these suggest the diversity of identities and interests within the person we know as 'Derek Jarman': furious at injustice of all kinds *and* green-fingered; at once raging *and* meditative, triumphantly gay *and* honouring of a distinct line within 'classical' English literature.

Instinctively intersectional decades *avant la lettre*, Jarman demonstrated unequivocally that the work and the life are one and indivisible. He embodied his own creativity so fully, warmly and generously* that readers and audiences could legitimately feel that they 'knew' him through his making: certainly those to whom his example most mattered loved rather than simply admired him. He showed what was possible if one fully trusted one's imagination (and teased out the often undeclared skills of those with whom one worked).

It is this endlessly fertile imagination that is fully on show here in his first – and only – prose fiction. From their own richly singular perspectives Michael Ginsborg, Philip Hoare and Declan Wiffen brilliantly inform this foundational text, which sees Jarman – dreaming, scheming, proposing – lay out his stall. Known previously only to close friends, his insightful biographer Tony Peake and intrepid archive explorers, this wandering, wayward tale finds Jarman at his most youthfully spirited and speculative. It is a huge pleasure and a privilege to be able to publish it here for the first time.

In an era of ideologically fuelled culture wars and attacks on the very idea of the arts from the government and from within managerially driven universities determined to marketise all they touch, it is more important than ever to consider Jarman's legacy, significance and influence while also celebrating how this remarkable life and work came into being. He shows us a more inclusive and internationalist, outward-looking England – one that acknowledges its own historical successes yet remains constantly vigilant regarding its oppressions, bigotries and flaws.

What the elder Jarman might have become we can only guess, but the young Derek we can meet now on these spirited pages and in his own miraculous reading, as if he were in the room with us.

Towards the grim, violent close of the 1930s Brecht also asked, 'In the dark times / Will there also be singing?' To which he gave his own reply: 'Yes, there will also be singing. / About the dark times.'

We move forward by remembering what matters, and bringing it with us for the journey. Onwards, through ...

—

* I experienced this in a very modest but unforgettable way when I attended the premiere of his film *Wittgenstein* at the Arts Cinema, Cambridge (a venue the philosopher himself had attended many times) on 30 January 1993, the day before what would be Jarman's penultimate birthday. The auditorium was full beyond capacity. I moved towards my own reserved seat only to find it occupied. The man in it had his back to me and was talking animatedly to a person next to him. I gently made an interjection to the man, suggesting he was in my seat, and was appalled at my gesture, terribly embarrassed to realise – when he turned around – that it was Jarman himself, mid-interview for the student newspaper. His energy and charm completely belied his advanced condition. I apologised profusely but he told me not to worry at all and, as soon as they had finished, invited me to sit in the seat now vacant. After the film commenced, he stayed watching and would occasionally lean over and give a kind of brief annotation to certain scenes, a form of whispered 'director's commentary'. I was a complete stranger to him (at that point, never having been a student in the city, I was working as a casual office assistant processing sheep and suckler cow subsidies for the then Ministry of Agriculture) but he displayed no hierarchy or disinterest, and it made a huge impression on me.

AUDIO LINK

To listen to an exclusive recording of Derek Jarman
reading the story – the recording from which the
version in this book was transcribed – please visit
the link below, or scan the QR code.

https://soundcloud.com/prototypepubs/sets/djttbpl/s-
QkKv2bpIrEf

ACKNOWLEDGEMENTS

House Sparrow Press comprises Jess Chandler (Publisher and Editor) and Gareth Evans (Editor). For this volume they give very special thanks to The Estate of Derek Jarman, John Akomfrah, Keith Collins, Rory Cook, Michael Ginsborg, Nigel Good, Robert Greer, Philip Hoare, Theo Inglis, Storm Patterson, Tony Peake, Aimee Selby, Ali Smith, Martin Thomas, James Torrance, Declan Wiffen, Amanda Wilkinson, the London Review Bookshop, and, of course, to the life, work, example and memory of Derek Jarman.

AUTHOR BIOGRAPHIES

Derek Jarman (31 January 1942 – 19 February 1994) was an artist, filmmaker, set/garden designer and gay rights activist. His numerous films, along with extensive writings, have been hugely influential across the arts and society. His garden at Dungeness has been acclaimed internationally as one of the most important of its kind. He is buried in the graveyard at St Clement's Church, Old Romney, Kent.

*

Gareth Evans is a London-based writer, editor, film and event producer.

Michael Ginsborg is an artist who lives in London, where he studied at the Central and Chelsea schools of art. He has held senior teaching posts at Ravensbourne and Birmingham Polytechnic and was, until 2003, Director of Studies at Wimbledon School of Art. He was instrumental in starting the first MA in drawing and the first Centre for Drawing in the UK. He has held solo exhibitions at the Lisson Gallery, London (1969); Serpentine Gallery, London (1973); and Acme Gallery, London (1980). From 1985 to 2004 he exhibited regularly at Benjamin Rhodes Gallery, London. He has made large-scale commissions at Linklaters Alliance, London, and at Glaxo Wellcome Medicines Research Centre, Stevenage. Recent solo exhibitions include the Drawing Gallery, London (2005); Galleria Immaginaria, Florence (2008); Wills Lane Gallery, St. Ives (2008); Artist of the Day, Flowers Gallery, London (2018). His most recent solo exhibition was held in 2022 at Benjamin Rhodes Arts, London, and consisted of a series of 52 drawings titled *Field Notes*.

Philip Hoare's books include biographies of Stephen Tennant and Noël Coward, *Wilde's Last Stand* and *England's Lost Eden*. *Spike Island* was chosen by W.G. Sebald as his book of the year for 2001. *Leviathan or, The Whale* won the 2009 BBC Samuel Johnson Prize for non-fiction, followed by *The Sea Inside* and *RISINGTIDEFALLINGSTAR*. *Albert & the Whale* (2021) led the *New York Times* to call the author a 'forceful weather system' of his own. In 2021 he co-curated *Derek Jarman's Modern Nature* at the John Hansard Gallery, Southampton, and he is co-curator, with Angela Cockayne, of the podcasts www.mobydickbigread.com and www.ancientmarinerbigread.com

Declan Wiffen is Lecturer in Contemporary Literature and Critical Theory at the University of Kent. He is editor of *Litmus: the lichen edition*, a magazine exploring the intersection of science, poetry, art and ... lichen; organiser of the writing workshops *Cruising the Estuary* and *Cruising Nature*; and a collaborator on The Unfiltered Coast, an arts project engaging young people in climate change. His pamphlet, *indiscriminate lanking*, was published by Invisible Hand Press.

ABOUT THE LONDON
REVIEW BOOKSHOP

The *London Review of Books* opened its bookshop in
May 2003. The shop has since established itself as one
of London's leading independent bookstores, maintaining
its commitment to the best writing through careful stock
selection, informed bookselling and a rich and varied
programme of author readings, talks and discussions.
It can be found, along with its excellent café, in the heart
of Bloomsbury, at 14 Bury Place, London WC1A 2JL,
or online, where it sells to a global readership
(www.londonreviewbookshop.co.uk).

HOUSE SPARROW PRESS

Formed in 2016 to publish *A Sparrow's Journey: John Berger reads Andrey Platonov*, House Sparrow Press is, in the best and multiple senses of the word (it is hoped), an 'occasional' venture. Based in Hackney, London, it seeks to publish creatively committed, collaborative works both at a time that is relevant and for reasons that feel compelling. It is drawn to manuscripts of hybridity, titles that might elude conventional publication over concerns of form or scale. It also believes in a modesty of style (but never of ambition) and a fecundity of ideas. Its moniker (drawn from its first venture) celebrates a creature that was once ubiquitous and yet is now threatened. The idea of a bird inhabiting and inspiring a place of residence also feels resonant. This is what the best books do too. There are wings at work here. In short, Emily Dickinson was right (again) when she observed that 'hope is the thing with feathers'.

Previously published titles are:

A Sparrow's Journey: John Berger reads Andrey Platonov (2016)

Infinite Gradation by Anne Michaels (2017)

Doorways: Women, Homelessness, Trauma and Resistance, ed. Bekki Perriman (2019)

Dialogue with a Somnambulist: Stories, Essays & a Portrait Gallery by Chloe Aridjis (2021)